WHY ME?

Leola Mae Harmon

Introduction by
James O. Stallings, M.D.

STEIN AND DAY/*Publishers*/New York

First published in 1982
Copyright © 1982 by J. O. S. Enterprises, Ltd.
All rights reserved
Designed by Louis A. Ditizio
Printed in the United States of America
STEIN AND DAY/*Publishers*
Scarborough House
Briarcliff Manor, N.Y. 10510

Library of Congress Cataloging in Publication Data

Harmon, Leola Mae.
  Why me?

  1. Face—Surgery—Patients—United States—Biography.
2. Harmon, Leola Mae.   3. Nurses—United States—Biography.
4. Surgery, Plastic.   I. Title.
RD523.H38   362.1'9752   [B]   81-40810
ISBN 0-8128-2844-5   AACR2

To Doctor James O. Stallings
and the others
who made my recovery possible

ACKNOWLEDGMENTS

Transfering memories of the most significant event in your life into book form is an awesome task and one I could not have achieved without significant contributions from a number of people.

The person who has had the greatest impact on my life—and the one most instrumental in producing this book—is Doctor James O. Stallings. Without his dedication, imagination, determination, unwaivering faith in himself and me, and particularly, his unsurpassed surgical skills, there would have been no story to tell. Not only did he restore my ravaged face, but, more important, he helped me gain a true sense of self worth. There are no words which adequately express my deep appreciation for his contributions to my life and for his encouragement and assistance in preparing this book.

The guiding force behind the completion of the book—from original concept to the final manuscript—was Merrick Scott Rayle, Doctor Stallings' attorney, advisor, and friend. With excellent judgment and high standards of professionalism, he has been tireless in his efforts on this project—encouraging, advising, and prodding, when necessary.

I am most appreciative for the suggestions and acute editorial judgments of Marcia Powell, Wayne Smith, and Mary Ruth Ottoson; and for the contributions of writers June Reno and Mary Anne Mackay—all of whom were invaluable.

Others who must receive special thanks are Cheri Pupp, who typed the manuscript; William Nye, for his thorough research; Sol Stein and Daphne Hougham of Stein and Day; Judy Palone of Marble Arch Productions; and my trusted attorney and friend, Harris Coggeshall.

Finally, I shall always be most grateful to all those wonderful people at Elmendorf Air Force Base whose friendship, encouragement, and professional skills gave me the hope and strength to continue.

INTRODUCTION

By James O. Stallings, M.D.

> We restore, repair, and make whole those parts of the face
> which nature has given but which fortune has taken away,
> not so much that they may delight the eye, but that they
> may buoy up the spirit and help the mind of the afflicted.
> —Gaspare Tagliacozzi, 1597

Afflicted was certainly the right word for Leola May Harmon on that fateful night in 1968 when the sounds from her blocked airway sent me hurtling through the emergency room doors and into what would become the most challenging and meaningful experience of my life.

At the time, my only thought was to try to save the life of a woman in acute danger. Once that was accomplished, I had time to assess the devastation wrought by fortune on this nurse. Her face below her eyes had been mutilated beyond recognition . . . but surely there was hope?

The average person would have been overwhelmed by the odds Leo faced. But she confronted them with a fierce determination to overcome all obstacles. During the months following her accident, Leo's courage was to inspire everyone with whom she came in contact.

Encouraged by Leo's example, all of us on the Elmendorf Air Force Base hospital staff became dedicated to doing everything humanly possible to justify her fighting spirit. Leo's case offered me, as a young surgeon, an unbelievable challenge to use skill, knowledge, and creative ability in restoring her face. It was an opportunity to right an enormous wrong perpetrated by fate, and it was with a mixture of excitement and profound humility that I set about the task.

Throughout all the physical and emotional suffering that I know Leo felt, she made a concerted effort always to appear in good spirits. There were periods of great despair, but determination always showed in her beautiful brown eyes, and I was equally determined to justify her faith in me.

What I learned through association with Leo has profoundly influenced me as a surgeon and as a person. Her quick intelligence and understanding of what I was trying to do and her willingness to travel into the unknown of surgery with me, inspired me to reach beyond the limits imposed by "customary" surgical procedures. When a task seemed impossible, Leo's faith urged me to open my mind for creative ways of turning impossibility into achievement.

Leo gave me my first real understanding of the depths of human courage, a quality I have seen displayed in many ways by many people since—but which has never equalled that of Leola Mae Harmon.

CHAPTER 1

I pointed the little red Mustang at the Chugach Mountains, navigated the turn onto Tudor Road, a two-lane highway, and checked the instrument panel as the car began the familiar slow climb. Bugler's last-minute improvised patch on the radiator seemed to be holding, which meant I would be on time. On surgical duty, lateness is simply unthinkable; and Elmendorf Hospital, where I was an Air Force nurse, lay just the other side of the mountains. I could feel the tension ease out of my neck, my grip on the wheel. Everything was going to be just fine.

The day was bright, clear, no wind, Celsius about zero. Four or five inches of snow lay on the sloping land. The stunted Alaskan pine forest that covered the mountain was lightly powdered. The road had been cleared but was wet . . . perhaps a trifle skiddy. I evened out my speed to a careful forty, five miles below the posted limit, even though the road was empty. A blue patch of Lake Otis sparkled in the distance.

I felt a smile play across my lips. "Well, you tried, Leola." I said it aloud. Alaska was not quite what I'd had in mind when I volunteered for Viet Nam, the starch barely dry on the pristine white cap issued upon my graduation from the Riverside White Cross Methodist Hospital School of Nursing. Of course, I could have volunteered as a civilian nurse. Others did. But I had enlisted in the Air Force on the spur of the moment, images of Danang, rubble and exhausted refugees, wounded GI's; pitiful children with bandages tangling in my mind. How innocent and naive I had been then in 1966 at the ripe old age of nineteen. It had certainly baffled everyone that Leola Harmon, hands down the best-looking girl in Pickaway County, Ohio, would just up and enlist in the Air Force because she had been moved by a plea on television. My smile widened at the memory.

The truth was, I had always confused everyone a little. Especially when I announced that I was going to leave home and become a nurse instead of settling down with one of the army of young men who had tried to win my undivided attention all through high school. It wasn't that I thought I was better than the girls who, married or otherwise, stayed in Circleville, it was more a matter of having always felt that there was something else I wanted to do in life. Something more. Something more important.

At first my stepmother treated my ambition to become a nurse as a phase; she was convinced that by the time graduation rolled around I would have found that special man and would be thinking of marriage, of raising a family. That's what everyone did, had done for generations. I wanted that too, but not yet. First I wanted to see some of the world, leave the familiar boundaries and see if there was another place for me, one where I might even do some good.

"Can't you be a nurse here, at home?" My stepmother's voice was plaintive.

"They *need* me in Viet Nam. They wouldn't be advertising on television if there weren't a terrible shortage of medical personnel."

"But it's so dangerous, Leola. I don't know why you don't just stay home."

"And get married? Have children?" I finished her thought.

She looked hurt. "Is there anything wrong with that?"

"No, of course not. I want that too. But I have to do this first."

"But Viet Nam? What if something happens?"

"Something will. That's for sure, and that's why I want to go. But nothing bad is going to happen. Not to Leola Harmon."

I believed that, with all my heart.

But instead of Viet Nam, the Air Force in its infinite wisdom had elected to ship me here, to Anchorage. At least I was doing something I liked; I was on surgical duty now. What's more, I was good at it. "Admit it, Leola," I said aloud. "More than anything, or anyone, you love your work." It was true. I loved it with a passion more intense than I'd ever felt for any man, including Gary. I could feel my face tighten at the memory of Gary last night. The arguments were becoming more frequent, erupting over the least little thing. Maybe I was pushing him too hard, expecting too much.

The road was straight now. I was running along the flat top of the mountain; the radiator was obviously going to be okay. It wouldn't do to be stuck out here in the middle of nowhere. I saw the bus when it was still half a mile or so away, just nosing around a curve. I perceived it as that unmistakable splash of chrome yellow that says one thing to any driver: school bus. As it drew rapidly nearer, I could see heads bobbing. Children jumping up and down inside, waving their arms. Hollering, no doubt. I felt a twinge of sympathy for the driver. My eye caught something else—something looming behind the bus, almost in its shadow. A pickup truck, tailgating—the fool! Oh, yes, I'm an observant driver—for all the good it did me that day.

The truck swung into my lane and picked up speed. My mind raced as it bore down on me. "Dear God, he's trying to pass! Can't he see me? . . . *Can't he see me coming?*"

Then I saw the driver slumped over the wheel, his mouth open. Some kind of attack—a seizure? Drunk? Not the moment for brakes. He was coming at me head on. I had to get out of his way. Orders to myself crackled through my brain: Don't hit the kids. *Don't hit the kids!*

I wrenched the wheel toward the twelve-foot embankment that shored up the right side of the road. Ah, Leola . . . you didn't make it: The Mustang took the direct impact on its port beam. The frame held. I saw the hood of the truck rear up in the air. "Dear God, it's going to land in my lap!" It sheered off; my back wheels swerved left. The Mustang and the truck, side by side as if in a pact, plunged off the embankment and smashed into a row of jackpines. *This can't be happening, not to me. Not to Lieutenant Leola Mae Harmon. What about Gary? You're married, remember? Okay, not to Lieutenant Leola Mae Harmon Cox.*

I have heard accident victims say that what in reality is only split

3

seconds is perceived as sequences expanding into infinity. They're right. It all went so slowly. I was wading through cold syrup. *Crack!*—the seatbelt snapped open, leisurely, parting like enormous black ribbons on a package. I was thrown forward against the windshield, then flung back. My face smashed down against the three-pronged steering wheel, the spinning spokes tearing methodically into my mouth and chin. I felt amazement at the violence of the impact rather than pain. Then indignation. "I'm going to be late for work!" A door flew open and I was hurled out into a cloud of white.

I'd often listened to patients tell—they always insisted on telling—about hanging midway between life and death. It always embarrassed me: poor deluded fools, thinking they've glimpsed Heaven. A few, for whom I had decidedly more sympathy, had reported hanging suspended over Hell.

Personally, I was amazed to find that Heaven was all white (I'd been led to expect a lot of gold and some blue): very white, very luminous. I was looking at a white meadow with white trees, a fruit orchard with crystal fruit, apples, cherries, pomegranates, grapes, all white. A silver-white river separated me from the meadows and orchards of Heaven. A bridge of spun glass arched over the river. I had one foot on the bridge and was about to start across when a white-robed figure with flowing silver hair—no wings—appeared before me.

The figure held up a hand. "Stop."

"But I have to cross here," I explained.

"If you think about it"—the voice was soothing—"you'll realize you don't really want to. Not yet. You have to go back."

I noticed to my surprise tht it was very cold in Heaven.

Snow. I was lying face down in a snow bank. I lifted my head. No, not snow. Snow isn't red. Then I remembered.

I knew I was injured but could feel nothing. Conscious but stunned, I tried to shift my body. A shaft of pain pierced my knee. I diagnosed myself: Probable broken leg. I noted that I was almost upside down, half in and half out of my car. The truck that had hit me lay on its side a few feet away. Nothing moving there.

4

In the distance, coming fast, I heard the intermittent squawk and bray of a squad car, the scream of a fire siren. Help on the way. I waited, careful not to move again. Both vehicles tore past in a shower of slush and gravel. I raised an arm and waved. A young man clinging to the back of the fire truck saw me.

"Back there!"

The squeal of heavy tires, halting. The grinding sound of axles making two very fast U-turns. Heavy boots crunching through the snow. I was rolled expertly onto a stretcher, turned face up. Silence.

"They could at least say hello," I thought giddily. I opened my eyes.

"It's alive!" A man's voice.

"It? It." Where was the appreciative, stroking glance that had always come my way whenever a new man looked at me? "What does he mean? *It.*" My throat was closing. Somebody better tell him "it" can't breathe.

I lost consciousness when they raised the stretcher. I have no memory of being loaded into the ambulance. Awareness left me like a torch receding into a long, dark tunnel. A sudden roar and a brilliant sheet of light jarred me back. Now another, larger body lay on an adjacent stretcher. Heavy snoring and fumes of whiskey permeated the close air. And through it a hoarse moan: "What have I done? Jesus, what have I done?"

The ambulance was rolling. From the window near my head I could see both wrecks and what looked like half the mountain forest in flames. One or both gas tanks. Goodbye, Mustang. I had bought it second-hand, financed by the Elmendorf Air Force Base Credit Union. It was the second Mustang I'd owned; the first slid off a muddy curve one wet spring morning back in Ohio, hit a tree and then a boulder. It was a total wreck but I and the two other passengers—one of them my stepmother—walked away without a scratch. I mourned the end of that car, which was why I had been so delighted to find another just like it, even to the candy-apple-red color.

The car salesman in Anchorage had listened indulgently to my tale of the wreck and the lucky escape. "I chose that car because it had a horse's name." I explained. "I love and trust horses more than I do a lot of people. That red Mustang took care of me. This one will too." Brave words. What did I know?

The ambulance attendant was looking at me strangely. Sensing my attention, he cleared his throat and spoke up. "Just like Scarlett O'Hara fleeing Atlanta." He ducked his head as he patted my hand.

This is no time for small talk. I can't breathe! Can't you see that? I gestured feebly at my throat.

He nodded. "I know, your windpipe is damaged. Hang on. We'll have you in Anchorage in no time flat the way Henry up there is driving. They'll trach you as soon as we pull in."

Not Anchorage. My mind screamed, take me to Elmendorf! Elmendorf! My very own hot-spit emergency room, the best in the world. Frantically I touched the lieutenant's bars on my uniform shoulders.

"I know, you're military. But Anchorage is closer." His voice was filled with assurance.

"Gluh—" That was all I could manage. No use, they were taking me to Anchorage, to the Eskimo Hospital.

"A hospital just for Eskimos?" That's what I had asked the eager young corporal who drove me to Elmendorf the day I landed in Alaska, eons ago.

"Naw," he said, "that's just what everyone calls it. It's the U.S. Public Health Hospital, for civilians. Elmendorf's 'way over there coupla miles. It's not even on the base—it's off by itself, for peace and quiet I guess. The Eskimo calls us for help when they get short-handed. You might find yourself there some time."

"What the devil!" I was lying on a mobile stretcher in what appeared to be a small lobby. A man in a white coat was bending over me. "What the devil!" He said it again. "Henry, you jackass, what did you bring her here for? She's military. On active duty, yet!"

"She's in bad shape, doc. She can't breathe."

I wondered vaguely where the attendant had gone, then his now-familiar voice chimed in. "She needs to be trached."

"We don't treat military here, you both know that."

"She'll strangle to death if you don't help her!"

"Pete, my Chief will strangle me if I do."

"For Christ's sake—"

"So now you're a doctor? Don't tell me what to do, I can't help her. It's against our policy. Load her back into the meat wagon and get her the hell out of here."

Back into the ambulance. As the doors were closing, the doctor hollered, "I'll phone Elmendorf and tell them you're on the way! Better do the trach yourself, Pete. Use a pen knife if you have to. Don't want her DOA when you get there—won't look good on your record!"

"Hold it!" Pete shouted. "Hold it, Henry!" He picked the whiskey-sodden truck driver up by his shoulders and pushed him out of the ambulance into the arms of the startled doctor. "Here," he snarled, "take this one! You'll *like* him, he's a civilian!"

The ambulance roared off again. I lifted my head and tried to focus on my fingernails. They were white with a tinge of blue. Some time now without enough oxygen. I was wheezing, beginning to make rattling noises. I knew what that meant.

Pete was opening a small black box. He drew out a trach knife and a tube, looked at them dubiously and then at me. "I've had the course," he said, "but I've never actually done it." A tracheotomy; a small v-shaped slit in the windpipe. Easy. Simple, Pete. Just be sure you put the knife in the right place. His face looked drawn, a muscle twitched along his jaw. He put the tools back in the box and snapped it shut. "Floor it, Henry."

"They already think we're the Chilkoot mail plane," said Henry. But he gunned the ambulance away from the Eskimo.

They were all waiting. Every blessed emergency crew member at the ready when I was wheeled in on the gurney; it halted under a big flaring ceiling light. They sighted my uniform.

"My God, it's one of ours!"

"It's Lieutenant Harmon."

"Leola? Christ!"

I couldn't believe what I was seeing. They stood immobile, frozen, so appalled they couldn't move. Then a man in whites was bending over me. I made out the Dental Corps insignia.

He opened my mouth. From the pain I knew my jaw was broken. My entire body was an anguished scream, but all I could release was one choked gurgle.

"Considerable malocclusion here. And some missing teeth . . . number sixteen, number twelve . . ."

My throat is in spasm, I'm dying, and this man is counting my teeth!

"Seems to be having a little trouble breathing . . ."

Lord, I can't stand this. Let me pass out now.

"Root canal will probably save numbers six and seven . . ."

You guys! Don't just stand there . . . you crazy? Seen you in action so many times. . . . Why are you gawking . . . do you think I'm dead? I'm about to be! Smothering . . . choking . . . do something . . . help me!

Suddenly I heard a double slam and a terrible crash. The doors to the emergency room were flung practically off their hinges and a tall, husky doctor I had never seen before fairly leaped across the floor.

"What in hell's the matter with all of you? Why isn't this patient trached? I could hear her rattling out in the hall. Get me a trach set!"

"Excuse me, doctor, I haven't finished my examination."

"Get out of my way!"

"This patient has a severe, imperative dental problem—"

"She's got a severe, imperative breathing problem, you jerk!"

"Do you know who I am?"

"No, and I hope for your sake I never find out. Nurse, get some pressure on those leg bleeders. Get a venocath in her. Blood and fluids. Tell X-ray to stand by—I'll need multiple angles, stem to stern. Set me up a cut-down. Suspend the saline. Needle, please, 24-d with 8 centies sofy amy."

The calm efficiency of his voice, the cool professional ease he exuded had freed the emergency crew from their paralysis and they were hopping to in proper style. The trach knife flashed in the light. I looked directly into his eyes. God, he must be an intern, he looks *much* too young to be a doctor . . .

"Here it comes." His voice was gentle, apologetic. "I can't wait for the beauty sleep to take hold. Hang on, here we go."

I hope you've done this before. My mind screamed the thought. Air. Delicious air. He had done it so deftly I barely felt a thing. Now glorious, sweet air was filling my lungs. He was grinning down at me as if he could read my thoughts.

I was told later that a gold crown from a back molar had been jolted loose and lodged in my windpipe. I never did find out who got the piece of gold that came so close to finishing me off. What a souvenir that would have been! The needle-induced beauty treatment was now lapping warmly and comfortingly around me. The last thing I remember is riding up in the elevator on the way to surgery. How ironic. It was to have been my duty. A soothing female voice filtered through the fog enveloping me, "Don't worry, Leo. I got hold of Gary. He's on his way." It was Daria. I felt her hand close over mine with infinite tenderness.

CHAPTER 2

As the elevator doors silently closed, Daria kept up a stream of conversation, her hand warm and reassuring around mine. I was touched by the muted anxiety I could hear in her voice. The anesthetic that had been administered in the Emergency Room was beginning to envelop me but I didn't want to go under, not yet. I fixed my eyes on Daria's in a concentrated effort to communicate.

"Dr. Stallings is already scrubbing. He looks like he's barely out of med school but everyone says he's unbelievably good. I heard he actually called the officer from the Dental Corps an ass and practically threw him across the E.R. Must have been quite a scene."

It was. Someday I'd tell her all about it. The fierce look in Stallings' eyes would be stamped indelibly on my mind forever. I squeezed Daria's hand weakly. I had so many questions, so many things to say. Daria returned the squeeze.

Stallings. Stallings. I'd heard about him too. But what? Oh, yes. He was always wanting the Operating Room, always wanting more time. Anesthesiology was up in arms because he wanted them to work longer hours. Administration was annoyed because he had said, repeatedly, that he didn't give a hoot in hell about Air Force regulations. Thank God for that. I wouldn't be breathing if he had stood on ceremony. I would have expired quietly while some dentist counted my molars. Next time I heard the scrub nurses gossiping about the brash young surgeon, I'd tell them a thing or two. There was something else about him, something I couldn't remember. . . . I was sinking slowly now, clinging to Daria's hand.

"We're notifying the family, Leo. I'm sure you'll want them with you."

With all the strength I could muster, I opened my eyes wide and tugged on Daria's hand.

"What is it? Don't you want them to come?"

I tried to make a sound and succeeded in emitting a horrible gurgle.

Daria was looking directly into my eyes. I tugged desperately, wondering why she wasn't responding. Weak, I'm too weak.

"You don't want them to come?"

I blinked for yes.

"They have to be notified, Leo. You know that."

I blinked again.

"But you don't want anyone to come?"

I blinked again. The gurney was being wheeled to the O.R. I felt her release my hand.

"Okay, Leo. I'll take care of it. Don't worry." I couldn't see her but knew she was watching as I was wheeled into the Operating Room. How different it looked from this angle. I was carefully placed on the table. The team was assembled, gowned and masked. I was too groggy to be frightened. A figure leaned over; I thought it was the anesthesiologist until I recognized those intense eyes above the mask. It was Stallings. Stallings. Now I remembered what it was I had heard: "He may be young, but he's already a master surgeon." The words rippled on waves through my mind as I sank slowly into the haven of unconsciousness. I was drifting to a safe zone in time and memory.

A green nurse newly arrived on the staff of a hospital, any hospital, expects to go through a certain amount of hazing. If you go through the experience in reasonably good cheer, without bursting into tears or blowing your stack, you are part of the team. I wasn't sure whether an Air Force hospital in wartime made room for such hijinks, but when I found I was assigned to ob-gyn—obstetrical-gynecology, an easy break-in—I was instantly on guard.

My supervisor at nursing school, herself a six-minute egg, had given me some parting advice. "Be tough if you have to, but never at the cost of losing your feminity. Show anger, if you must, but never at the price of your dignity. If the joke is on you, shake your head and walk away from it. Above all, look around right away for a friend, a good woman friend who has a little seniority on the staff."

I looked around on the first day at Elmendorf and found Daria. Or, rather, she found me. She tapped on the door of the cubicle they called my bedroom in Bachelor Officers Quarters and walked in, smiling.

"Hello, I'm Daria Lewis—welcome aboard. I took a look at your accreditation papers and saw your special training is in cardiac recovery. Naturally that prompted the great minds who decide these things to put you in obstetrics with me. Makes sense."

I smiled and put my hand out awkwardly, remembering my training. Back home in Circleville women rarely, if ever, shook hands with each other. We eyed each other for a long moment. Daria's grasp was firm and I liked what I saw: direct gray eyes; short, very pale blond curls; a sprinkling of freckles on an upturned nose. Her pierced ears held small hoop earrings in what I knew was a mild violation of the dress code—only studs were permitted. In the mirror behind Daria I caught sight of my own shiny mop of dark red hair and the wideset, deep brown eyes that had been compared on one occasion to the hearts of pansies and, on another, to Ohio River mud. My eyes met Daria's and we both laughed.

"We make a pretty striking pair, too bad we can't go prowling together." She held up her left hand to show me a gold wedding band. "I'm married. But not to worry, I'll introduce you around. I suppose I don't have to remind you that you're an officer and a gentleman, no fraternizing with enlisted men."

"I had a sergeant in Little Rock who made that more than clear. I quote, 'As far as the Air Force is concerned you get the treatment, the privileges and the hazards of men. You are not women but female officers and gentlemen.' "

Daria laughed. "I think all sergeants grew up on the same movies, they always act the part to perfection. But I guess they had to be tough; the bottom line is that any one of us could be sent onto the battlefield and ordered to serve under fire."

"And for all their tough talk, here we are. I volunteer for Viet Nam and wind up here in ob-gyn."

"The Air Force never ceases to amaze me. Tried on your whites yet?"

"No, I was just about to."

"Good, I'm glad I got here in time. Unless I'm very mistaken, you're going to need some moral support."

I slipped out of my uniform and donned the nursing whites that had been spread out on the bed. I adjusted the skirt, then checked the mirror. "Phooey, they gave me the wrong size. These are miles too big."

"No, they're the right size," Daria sighed. "Try to think of it as Air Force chic."

"But I can't go around looking like this. You can't tell what's inside. I'm all square. Look at me, I look like a refrigerator."

"Hardly a refrigerator with a face like yours. Even the design, or lack of it, can't disguise the fact that you're a knockout."

I peered unhappily in the mirror. "If you ask me, I look pretty dowdy. Obviously your husband never saw you in your whites, otherwise he might never have given you a second glance."

"Come to think of it, he did. He was a convalescing navigator. I know that's a movie cliché, but we did meet at bedside. Obviously he's a man of great vision. When he told me I was a good nurse, I knew he really meant it."

"I want to be more than a good nurse." I was surprised and a little embarrassed at the earnestness in my voice.

Daria nodded thoughtfully, "I know the feeling."

And I knew that she did. I knew she was more than a good nurse. "I want people to say, 'Leola, you're a damned good nurse!' I want to be memorable."

"You'll probably get your chance here."

I did my time in obstetrics and moved on to the general medical-surgical wards. From Viet, Elmendorf was the closest home station other than Hawaii. Ambulance planes, sometimes as many as ten a day, roared in with casualties. The burn cases were the worst—boys with torched-out ears, noses, even throats. Patients who were reasonably stable stayed at Elmendorf for continuing treatment and some initial reconstruction. Those cases were evaluated as more serious ones were given sustaining therapy and airlifted back home.

I began to sleep, eat, and breathe my work, and seemed well on my way toward realizing my ambition.

"You've got to hang loose, Leola," Daria said over coffee one morning. "Detach or you're going to burn yourself out."

"I can't help it. No one at home has any idea what's going on, what's happening. You know there aren't enough who care or understand. I've got to make it up to these guys."

"Leo, stop it. If you don't, I'll pull rank and have you transferred back to ob-gyn where it's a lot more cheerful."

"Sure it's more cheerful—there's no real suffering among those patients. Just temporary pain, and a bundle of joy at the end of it. These guys from Viet have nothing but despair at the end of their pain. They—"

"Oh, balls, Leola! You'd better get it through your head that you belong with your patients while you are on your shift. If you stay with them mentally during off-hours, you'll find yourself in a bed on the funny farm. What you need," she prescribed, "is a night on the town. Put on your slinkiest dress, one that shows off that dynamite figure of yours. I'll round up some of the girls and we'll go pub crawling and see what amusements we can find."

I knew Daria was right. I was seeing pretty raw stuff for a young nurse and had begun to feel nervous and look drawn. Maybe a break in routine would help.

"But your husband—"

"Bob? He's all for it, in fact he's the one who suggested a night on the town. In fact, he wants to come along. We can keep a discreet distance, we'll be invisible chaperones in case anybody gets too strange. Come on, now, see you at eight o'clock!"

For this dear, new sister I was ready to do anything. I wasn't about to tell her that I had never been in a bar in my life, escorted or unescorted. My family is small-town Methodist and absolutely teetotal. It was sometimes whispered that my uncle Jed on my mother's

15

side had once been a drunk, but he apparently took the pledge long before I was born. I had once sipped at a glass of sherry so genteelly offered that I couldn't find polite enough words to refuse. It couldn't have been a very good sherry; I thought it tasted pretty much like argyrol, a standard throat swab.

That evening I allowed half an hour for putting on makeup, an undertaking which normally occupied something under five minutes. As I checked the results in the mirror, I felt I had overdone it. My Vaselined and curled eyelashes made me look, I thought, unnaturally starry-eyed: too many lashes, too much pressure with the curler, not enough practice. Oh well, by the time we reached town the lashes would have relaxed even if I hadn't.

I put on a soft wool jersey that was dark orange, a radical color for a redhead, and piled into a minibus with eight or ten other nurses. Daria and Bob followed in their sporty little MG.

"Are we going to the Officers Club?" I asked one of the girls.

She sketched a rectangle in the air with her forefinger. "Too square. All they talk is flying."

"What's wrong with that?"

"Nothing, really. But most of them are married. Besides, the Club closes at 11:30." We were getting off the three-to-eleven shift. I sank back in my seat as the minibus jolted its way into Anchorage, listening to a rowdy chorus of "Off we go, into the white mush yonder, look out boys, here come the girls . . ."

Anchorage was still badly scarred from the earthquake and tidal wave of two years before. I could see rubble and wreckage in some streets. Much of the hasty new building was ramshackle and shoddy. Houses built on stilts for flood protection looked like mechanical monsters when they were lit up at night. In the sky, the stars were all in the wrong places, very confusing, because we were so far north. In the streets, the damned snow lay piled in dirty heaps at the curbside. And over all was a multicolored glare of neon that beckoned luridly: DANCE! DRINK! BAR! SHOW! EAT! DANCE!

That's what I'll do, I thought as I climbed out of the bus feeling like a teenager out on her first date. I smoothed my dress, touched my earlobes to be sure Grandma's garnet earrings were still in place, took a deep breath and walked through an open door beneath a sign bearing the legend OLD TYME GOLDRUSH SALOON.

A wave of music enveloped me, the rhythm tugged at my body and I experienced a sharp, giddy sense of elation. A line of young men at the bar turned and smiled as we approached. Among the eager faces I recognized a few medical corpsmen from the hospital. Enlisted men.

"Hi," said one of them, grinning foolishly. "Imagine seeing you here, Lieutenant." His face was red; mine was all smiles. The juke box throbbed with "Let the Sunshine In." Why not? I decided to forget all about being a female officer and gentleman.

"Hi," I answered. My voice was trembling a little, but I had the feeling it would straighten out soon.

I wasn't the toast of Anchorage. Nor did I want to be, although it would have been easy enough to manage. The ratio of men to women must have been about a hundred to one—open season for the truly free spirits. No doubt my upbringing had a lot to do with my reticence, and there were moments when I envied the ease with which other nurses moved in and out of casual relationships.

"You're more serious than you realize," Daria said. "It has nothing to do with being a prude or a stick-in-the-mud or small-town Ohio. I think it's refreshing."

"Sometimes it worries me that I just can't let go and have a good time. It really bothers me when a guy feels he can paw over my body just because I agreed to dance with him."

"They're all trying to eat, drink, make merry, all that stuff. It goes with the territory. My personal opinion is that most of them are scared to death."

"Maybe."

"Just relax and enjoy yourself. God knows you need some distraction, the way you work."

"I think my family worries. I'm twenty years old, you know."

Daria laughed. "Practically an old maid."

I flushed. "By Circleville standards that's just what I am."

She looked at me thoughtfully. "*You're* not worried, are you?"

17

"A little. I wonder if something is wrong with me when I don't thrill to a man's fingers opening my blouse."

"You mean that guy in the bar? He was an out-and-out clod. There's nothing wrong with you."

"I seem to be searching for something, someone. I don't know what, or who."

"I know," said Daria. "I used to feel the same way. But you'll know when the time comes, you really will."

"I hope so."

It was months before I went into Anchorage again. I decided to inquire about other activities, outdoor sports; the facilities were too distant. And with all the damn snow around, no one even pretended to enjoy it. Then I bought the candy-apple-red Mustang. It was instant love. I've always had a tendency to fall in love with objects, usually without regard to their value. My real mother's gold bracelet, dented because I had teethed on it; an iron skillet that never ever burned anything; my first pair of riding boots; a faded miniature of a nameless ancestor painted on ivory—beloved objects, all.

As it turned out, the car didn't cheer me up as much as I thought it would. I drove around listlessly, scowling at the scenery. I was discontented and couldn't say why. Something was missing from my life, and I hadn't a clue as to what it might be.

"It's your first Alaskan winter, Leo—the cold and dark and snow seem endless," Daria said. "Lots of people go bananas toward the end of it. Come spring, the day the ice breaks, you'll feel better."

But I didn't. When the thaw came I was still frozen in a state of near despair. Except when I was working. I felt unreal, uncommitted to anything but my work.

And that was paying off; I was becoming a really good nurse able to interpret on the subtlest levels, make intelligent decisions that were beginning to earn me the respect of everyone, patients as well as doctors.

My nursing supervisor, Captain Laura Gwizk, a woman who was later to have a profound effect on my life, called me in after a particularly dramatic day in Emergency when my thinking quickly on my feet had saved a patient.

"You're a good sling nurse, Lieutenant." The slang phrase was

18

used to describe an all-around reliable professional. High praise indeed, and from Captain Gwizk, most unusual. "I've been looking over your dossier," she continued. "I see your student training pointed you into cardiac and you state that this is what you want to do."

I was too surprised to respond. The military was aware of what I wanted? And cared?

"We have decided to send you part time to Anchorage Community College for further study—156 hours—of arrhythmia interpretation and advanced EKG. Report there Wednesday at sixteen o'clock for enrollment and thereafter as required. Dismissed." She immediately returned to the papers on her desk.

I saluted smartly and did my best to contain my joy. My own heart was manifesting symptoms of arrhythmia—beating wildly in my chest. I had been recognized. I was on my way to being what I had told Daria I wanted to be: memorable.

Daria beamed at the news. "It's about time! What do you say—should we go out and celebrate? I'll call Bob and see if he wants to come, or we can go prowling just the two of us."

"You think he'd let you?"

"Sure. He knows as well as I do that it's perfectly safe out there. After all, we are . . ."

I laughed. "I know, officers and gentlemen."

I don't remember the name of the bar where I met Gary—which is surprising because, as Daria said pointedly on more than one occasion, I am "such a sentimental ass!" Despite the names—HONKY TONK HEAVE HO, SAWDUST AND SUDS, all wonderfully decadent and whimsical—the bars are really all alike. Decadent they are not. The Air Force MPs see to that. In fact, if you're anticipating the rough-and-tumble wantonness so often associated with last outposts or frontiers, Alaska as a whole will disappoint you.

What I do remember is that Gary was leaning against a bar, that's for sure, with the easy stance of a man at home in his environment. I had driven ahead of Daria and Bob, who were following in their MG. I felt like flying, but I was a good driver. Careful if not conservative. I knew exactly how much pressure on the gas pedal would keep me rolling at the right speed, crowding the limit a little

19

but never really exceeding it. Exactly the way I managed my life. Or so I thought.

Daria and Bob and I celebrated for an hour or so and when it came time to head for home, I told them to go ahead; I was still too keyed up with the prospect of advanced cardiac courses. Several other nurses I had come to know on previous forays into Anchorage had joined us and were still in a partying mood. Shortly after Bob and Daria left, we moved on to another bar.

That was when I spotted Gary. He looked at me without much interest when we walked in, but something about the stance intrigued me. The insouciance of the glance was, I now realize, a challenge. One that I couldn't resist in my elated mood.

"For starters," I whispered to Fran Perkins, one of the shyer and newer nurses in our crew, "I'm going to make sure that guy notices how attractive I am and, at the same time, get across the fact that I'm respectable."

"How in the world do you do both at the same time?"

"Just watch. You have to come on but come on softly and then, when you've got him interested, establish that you're decent."

"How do you do that?"

I didn't have the heart to tell her that my words of wisdom had, courtesy of Daria, been spoken to me barely an hour ago. "Leo," she said, leaning across the table, "the reason you're having trouble connecting with a man is you come across too hot or too cold." She then elaborated with the statement I had just passed on to Fran. Now I was momentarily stumped. How *did* you project availability and respectability at the same time?

"Oh, there are any number of ways," I said. "You can always say you have someone back home. That gives you a little leeway in case you want out."

At the moment, I wanted *in*. I had gotten a good look at the man—he was still halfway across the room—and my heart had stood still. Just like the silly song, a fine thing for a cardiac nurse! His manner was reckless, and yes, definitely intriguing.

"He looks like trouble to me, Leo. Maybe you should wait a while."

"I can handle it," I said cheerily. And I was sure I could. I hadn't felt this giddy since high school; besides, he looked like a taller version of Dustin Hoffman. There was an exciting intensity about him for all the studied casualness of that pose.

"Oh my God, Leo. Here he comes."

My breath caught as he bore down. No question about it, he had noticed me.

"How're you doing?" The voice was vibrant, and I remember nodding. Then, with perfect ease, not waiting for a reply, he danced me away from the wide-eyed Fran.

He moved beautifully; it was as if I had been dancing with him all my life. I don't remember much conversation—if indeed there was any—until he said, "How about a weekend in Seattle?"

"You sure work fast," I heard myself say in a voice that didn't sound like my own. I could almost hear Daria groan and was glad she wasn't there to witness the scene. I collected my wits and announced in my most proper tone: "And you're going too far."

"I know exactly how far to go when I'm going too far," he quipped.

"That can't be original. You're quoting someone."

"You're probably right. But who?" The expression on his face was so comically confused that we both broke up laughing.

I thanked him for dancing with me, gathered my things and left. As I drove back to the base I thought, "He's fun to be with. A charmer, but at the same time very direct. And what a dancer! Admit it, Leola. You like him a lot!"

"What's his name?" Daria asked as I described the encounter.

"Gary Cox."

"Military?"

"Of course. In fact you may even know him, he's in ob-gyn."

"Never heard of him, what's he do?"

I didn't want to tell her he was a newly arrived medical corpsman. She pried the information out of me.

"Leo, I'm not going to lecture you, but he is an enlisted man. Do you think it's wise?"

"It's nothing serious, we just danced, that's all. I haven't had such a good time in I don't know how long. He really is fun, what's the harm in dancing with him?"

"There's dancing and then there's dancing. Just be careful, Leo."

Gary and I never actually had a formal date. We continued to meet casually in Anchorage as though by happenstance. The banter was always light; the dancing, tireless. I was beginning to look forward to seeing him. I was even looking for him. No one except Daria seemed to know much of anything about him.

"He ties one on occasionally, Leola."

"Leola? Are you trying to tell me something, is this a formal reprimand?" I immediately regretted the annoyance in my voice. Daria was the least judgmental human being I had ever met. Now she looked hurt. "I'm sorry, Daria. What do you mean, ties one on'? Who told you that?"

She shrugged, "It's probably not important. I guess I'm afraid you'll get hurt."

"He does like to get high, I've noticed that. He's lonely, the poor kid. He can change. He needs motivation."

"He's nearly two years younger than you are."

"You really did check him out, didn't you?"

She shrugged again. "He doesn't sound like the marrying kind."

"You mean because he likes the bars? To party?"

"Well, isn't that true?"

"Yes, I suppose you could say that. But if you only knew him, Daria, you'd see how really unpretentious he is. He makes no bones about being from a poor Alabama family, about anything in his life. There's so much he wants to learn, to do."

"How serious is this?"

I had asked myself that same question, more than once, I knew it was serious the night he told me that he professed no religion at all. My heart sank with the knowledge that the news would not go over well in Ohio. This wasn't just a little excursion into research and development far from home and from Circleville codes of behavior. "It's serious."

"I see." That's all she said.

Gary had enlisted after landing a civilian job at an airfield in Florida. It hadn't taken him long to see that the military men doing almost the same work had all the perks. He, like me, was surprised and not too happy to find himself in Alaska. "A long way from poincianas," was the way he put it one night. He reached out and touched my hair. His touch was gentle; his eyes devoured me hungrily. "But somehow Alaska doesn't seem a bad place to be these days."

While it was reasonably clear that he was really smitten—and completely obvious that he thought I was the most beautiful woman he had ever seen—Gary wasn't all that easy to catch.

"I don't understand it," I told Daria. "I can almost see the electricity coming from him. He's so intense that sometimes I feel as if I'm going to melt."

"Ah, chemistry," said Daria.

"Well, there is that, but I feel something more in him. Something he won't put into words."

"Maybe he can't."

"What do you mean?"

"I don't know. Could be he's too overwhelmed, doesn't believe that anyone who looks like you could really be interested in him."

That thought hadn't occurred to me, and I doubled my efforts to make Gary feel more at ease. He began to shed the mantle of insouciance I had found so appealing in the beginning and I saw just how vulnerable he really was. There was no mistaking the look in his eyes, he was in love. I was, too. In love with the lost boy in the man. I resolved to be patient, to just let things unfold.

One night as we waited for our drinks to be served at a small corner table, he presented me with a ring, a small opal. "Just a friendship ring," he said as he slipped it on my finger. Opals are the gem of tears, unlucky. That's what my grandmother had once said. I tried to shake the memory. Superstitious nonsense. The blue-gray depths of the gem were full of warm, pink points of light.

"A *friendship* ring?" Daria said as she admired it. "This *is* getting serious."

"I don't know if it is or not. I do know he's in love with me. No one has ever looked at me the way he does."

"Well, you *are* beautiful, Leo. You must know that."

"I know, but the look I'm talking about is different. I mean, it's as if he thinks I'm the most gorgeous creature who ever walked on earth. It's hard to resist anyone who feels that way, it really is. Besides, he *isn't* the marrying kind. You were right about that. I've just decided to enjoy him and not worry about where it will lead."

"A wise decision."

"You really don't like Gary, do you?"

"It isn't that. He has loads of charm, he's great fun, a terrific dancer, and he's obviously mad about you. But marriage requires more than that, a lot more." She looked away. "He's awfully young for his age and there's just something about him I can't quite put my finger on."

I was touched by her concern but continued to see Gary.

Then, quite suddenly, Gary began to get serious. We set a wedding date: January 20, 1968. Daria said nothing at first, then hugged me, her eyes leaking tears. I telephoned home with the news. My stepmother was disappointed that we weren't planning to marry in Ohio. "Why can't you have the wedding here?"

"We can't get leave at the same time." I knew why I was lying. I knew my family would take one look at this man and put a stop to the whole thing. I also knew I thought he was the best I could do. Besides, we had a lot of fun together—and he needed me.

Daria agreed to be my matron of honor. Her chief, Dr. Gills, who had also been my first boss at Elmendorf, would give me away. They say all brides-to-be have moments of grave self-doubt; I certainly did. But I told myself that I could straighten Gary out. That once we were married, he would have the incentive to change, to grow up.

The rites were performed by a Protestant chaplain in the base chapel. At practically the last moment it developed that Gary had forgotten to buy my wedding ring. I jumped into the Mustang, tore into town, chose and paid for a ring myself. I simply pointed at the nearest gold band and said, "This one."

"Do you want it engraved, Lieutenant?"

"Yes. 'Eternity.'"

"Two days."

"Can't wait. I'll take it with me."

My wedding gown was my Air Force dress uniform. Daria pressed it for me. As the steam iron hissed, she said, "Just think, your grandchildren will go up in the attic one rainy day to see Granny Leola's wedding gown and instead of tulle and lace out will come this man-tailored suit with the gold buttons!"

"God only knows what they'll be wearing by then. Besides, it will tell them something about our times." I was rather pleased with the thought.

Gary had found a small furnished apartment on the outskirts of Anchorage. It was on the other side of the city from the base, a little inconvenient but that made it cheap. I bought a joint wedding present—good silk-screen prints of Degas ballerinas—and hung them on the walls of Apt. 6-B, 123 Seward Highway. I moved out of Bachelor Officers Quarters an hour after the wedding. We honeymooned in our new place, eating pizza and drinking beer.

My husband's first request was a simple one: "Honey, always keep plenty of beer on hand."

"I promise."

I have to admit that the next few months were stormy. It didn't help much to complain to Daria, who took a hard line. On me.

"You forget, you were the one who was so sure you could straighten him out. You can't expect to take a cute-looking, sexy guy who's halfway along the road to becoming a bum and turn him inside out tomorrow, the way you would a reversible jacket."

"He's not a bum!"

"Well, a not-too-motivated young man might be more accurate. All I'm trying to say is, given his background and inexperience, he's going to need time. Be patient."

"My patience is running thin. There's more to life than sitting around and drinking beer."

"Leola," Daria asked softly, "why *did* you marry him?"

She looked at me and I felt stripped. My eyes began to sting with tears. "I don't know."

"Well, I don't want to sound like a pill, but let's face it, you could have had any man you chose. Why Gary?"

I looked down at my hands. "He wanted me so."

Daria's brow furrowed. "And now that he has you, he doesn't know what else to go for in life?"

"I guess you could say that. Sometimes I get the feeling that he thinks he's inadequate."

"That could be. After all, you've got brains as well as looks. You're tops in your field, you're disciplined, energetic—there's no telling where you can go with your career. That can be a pretty intimidating combination for a man."

"I hadn't thought of it like that. Maybe I'm expecting too much from him."

"That may be all it is. He needs a decent break and with you he has a chance for a future."

"You really think so?"

"Seems logical. Maybe you can encourage him to go to school."

It took some doing, but I did manage to persuade Gary to enroll in college courses—Liberal Arts—to broaden his interests—a business degree—so he could make some real money somewhere, some day. At first he responded with enthusiasm. He bought a desk, a green-shaded lamp, a fancy pencil sharpener. Learning came easily; his early grades were good. Then, unaccountably, he began to slack off; I wound up doing most of his homework. He began to oversleep and cut classes. He overslept because of all the beer he was drinking. Resentment flamed into quarrels that were drowned, first in my tears, then in his beer, and, finally, reconciled in bed.

The honeymoon was over. In occasional moments I was able to back off and view my marriage as if I were an outsider looking in. I began to see what Daria had seen all along: a spoiled, lazy, immature if promising young man married to a smarty-pants nurse who had probably made a wrong decision and who was never, ever going to admit it. Then, somewhere in my head, a big band began playing "I took one look at you, that's all I had to do . . ." My own heart would

26

stand still, all over again, and I would feel hopeful. After all, we were both headstrong and had a lot of adjusting to do.

With all of this, I was doing better work than ever at the hospital, and I knew it. My enlistment was nearing its end, and I had two years' worth of extraordinary memories to carry with me back into civilian life. Perhaps the most memorable person I had met at Elmendorf was an eight-year-old boy named Michael. He had been born with just about every birth defect on the charts: crippled, twisted, uncoordinated, grossly misshapen, with a brain that didn't always function normally. He had long been the pet of the ward and became a very special pet of mine. His ability to communicate was limited; it flashed on and off and often seemed trapped in some remote, unreachable corner of his mind. At other times his ideas burst forth with astonishing brightness. Unlike Gary he was an eager student, receptive and hard-working. I began to teach him to read.

"Dammit, Leo, I'm sick and tired of your holding that kid up to me all the time."

"But Gary, he has so little going for him and you have everything. If you could just see how hard he tries."

"I don't want to see him, okay? Just get off my back. If you'd stop pressuring me everything would be fine. If you don't like me the way I am, why in hell did you marry me?"

"You know why I married you. I love you."

"Then stop bugging me. I have to do things in my own time."

"Our enlistments are up soon, yours before mine. We really have to think about where we're going from here, Gary."

"Warm. Wherever it is, it has to be warm." Gary opened a beer. "It's this damn cold that gets me down. I want to be somewhere where there's money, music, plenty of excitement, time and sunshine. And no snow whatsoever."

That was it! Alaska was a hostile climate for Gary. It was clear he needed love and warmth and time to recover from the long bleak winters. I would see to it that he got what he needed. Our world was an open road. A good nurse could get a job anywhere. And I was very, very good at keeping people alive.

Late in August, I walked into the office of a young internist in charge of new patients in General Medical. I was tired and feeling out of sorts. I had been working two shifts the past few weeks, Elmendorf plus a half-shift at the Eskimo.

"I don't like the looks of this patient, Doctor," I handed him a chart. "The corporal just came in from Danang. He's got something new on top of the bum leg. Low fever, and, all of a sudden, a nasty rash. I was with him for two hours yesterday and he didn't have it then."

The doctor rose from his desk, accompanied me into the ward and examined the patient.

"For Pete's sake, Lieutenant, what do they teach you in nursing school? Don't you know a simple case of German measles when you see one?"

"Measles? How can you get German measles in Viet Nam?"

"Beats me. But there were two other cases in the same planeload." I walked back with him to his office and stood in front of his desk. A large daily date calendar, its facing page covered with scribbles, stared up at me. A computer began ticking in my head. The date. The queasy stomach in the mornings. The occasional dizziness. The meaningless tears. My time in ob-gyn.

"Ever had German measles?" asked the internist as he sank into his chair.

"No."

"Good thing you aren't pregnant."

Early on the evening of November 7, Gary and I began to quarrel. It raged for hours. When we were too tired to go on, we'd stop for twenty minutes or so—long enough for Gary to down another beer, for me to cry. I even swung at him at one point. He responded by pushing me into a chair. "Let's try to have a reasonable discussion," he said.

"Impossible with you." I realized I was shrieking. I knew I couldn't win and I knew I couldn't stop.

"Leo, I refuse to father a blind baby! Or a monster!"

"*You're* the monster!"

"You think so? Picture the happy mother with her little boy— only look, it can't see and its arms don't work."

28

"You—!"

"Leola, if you swing at me again, I swear I'll lock you in the closet. I never hit a woman in my life but you just might be the first!"

Some time near the dawn of what promised to be a bright, clear day, we crept into bed, exhausted. My last thought before falling asleep was of Dr. Gills, chief of ob-gyn, the man who had given me away in marriage. "Either way, Leola, I'll be with you. But it's your decision. Yours alone."

The alarm went off at 7 A.M., squalling like a hungry infant. I reached out to punch it off. Nov. 8 twinkled at me cheerily from the date slots on the clock face. Cheerily but firmly. The clock had been a wedding present from Captain Laura, my nursing supervisor, who thought with good reason that I needed a top-quality, never-fail alarm clock. Gary was stretched out against me, warm, still sound asleep.

"It's that time," I said. The dreadful words we had hurled at each other the night before had been left in the living room. Gary's hand was curled around mine. Let not the sun go down upon your wrath, my grandmother always said. I could remember last night's anger but no longer felt it.

I shook his shoulder gently. "Better haul it," I murmured. "You've got that English Lit exam at ten-thirty and you wanted to get up early and cram."

Gary pulled the gray blanket over his head. "Fuck the exam." His voice was muffled. There is no suitable reply to an obscenity except another obscenity, which he knew I wouldn't use. It was his most effective way of saying, "Don't talk to me."

I picked up the rumpled, tear-stained, coffee-blotted uniform blouse I had hurled in a corner, carried it to the bathroom, laundered it in the wash bowl with the Roger et Gallet bath soap someone had given me the week before. I examined the collar carefully before hanging it up to dry. Captain Laura had a way of springing doorsill inspection on us, and if there was anything she hated it was ring around the collar.

I dressed in corduroy jeans, a cotton turtleneck and an intricately patterned sweater recently arrived from Reykjavik. Another cold place, half a world away. I put on boots.

29

"I'm going shopping," I announced to the hump in the bed. "Be back before noon. I'm on three-to-seven today. Better get up, if you're going to get up at all."

"Goodbye," Gary muttered from the bed. "Have a good day."

Junior won't go to school because he hasn't studied for his test. I looked at him again. He hadn't even opened his eyes. I light-stepped out of the apartment and locked the door behind me.

I decided to splurge at the supermarket, knowing full well that what I was really buying was a sense of power over circumstances I couldn't control. I bought comfort foods, not staples, stowed two large grocery bags of solace (including lavender bath salts) in the trunk of the Mustang, hopped behind the wheel and drove to the library. I browsed a bit, finally selecting two books—an Agatha Christie and a copy of *The Ski Bum*.

A traffic jam stalled me opposite the concert hall entrance to the municipal auditorium. As the engine idled I looked out the side window and watched two workmen slapping up a large pink poster. Anita Quinn plays Chopin. Never heard of her. Wait a minute. Yes, I have. She must be the wife of that new surgeon. What's his name— not Quinn. There had been an item in the base weekly paper when he arrived last August. Stallings, Major James Stallings. Yes, that was it. He had a wife named Anita who was a concert pianist and would give recitals here. No one had paid much attention. All that registered was that Major Stallings had a wife. The single girls promptly forgot him.

The light changed and I moved forward again. Plays Chopin. I respected classical music because I knew I was supposed to. But I didn't know anything about it. Poor Anita, she's a long way from Carnegie Hall. She'll be lucky to fill the front rows.

When I got back to the apartment, Gary was gone. Not long gone. His hollow in the unmade bed was still a little warm. I made the bed and unpacked the groceries, then flapped a feather duster over the furniture. Nurses are notoriously casual housekeepers. We're fast food addicts, too, even though we know all about nutrition. I was hungry and wished I had thought to pick up a hamburger. I quickly opened a jar of artichoke hearts and speared one with a fork.

I set up the ironing board, turned on the iron and began to press my uniform blouse. There was a sizzling noise, a burned smell and a wedge-shaped scorch.

"Damn!" Well, too late now; it would have to pass. Fortunately the burn was on the back and low down. I couldn't envision even Captain Laura yanking out my rear shirttail for inspection. Or would she? I put on my uniform, adjusted my cap.

I tossed off half a cup of cold coffee, finished the artichokes, went downstairs and climbed back into the car. It refused to start. Why? Ten minutes later I had used up my flimsy store of automotive knowledge without finding a clue to the problem. Then, down the street, I saw a neighbor approaching, a man I knew was a mechanic in the base HQ motor pool. I rolled down the window.

"Hey, Bugler!" I called. "Come over here, please. I've got a problem."

Bugler earned his nickname because you could hear his laugh from a closed room three blocks away and he was always laughing, mostly at his own jokes. He hurried across to the car, threw me a half-salute in acknowledgment of my uniform. "Whatsa trouble, Lieutenant? Finance company take the motor out? Ha ha!"

"Nothing that simple."

He raised the hood, fiddled around a few minutes and then said, "Okay, I see what it is. It's your radiator. I can give you a temporary patch here, good enough to get you to work. But you'd better catch a ride home. I'll send the general's do-nothing squad over to fix it in the morning. Be right back. Gotta go get some chewing gum and a bandaid." He trotted away.

A master, that Bugler. Twenty minutes later I was rolling along Seward Highway toward Elmendorf Hospital, 12 miles away. I glanced at my watch and chuckled.

I'm going to be on time. Right on time! The whole staff will drop dead in a faint!

Since about the age of ten, I've seldom been on time for anything. I'm either too early or more than a little late. Usually, if my appointment involves people I feel comfortable with, I'm late. If I'm to cope with strangers, I make sure to be there first. I'd been chewed out several times about being late at the hospital. And rightly so. It isn't much fun for the nurse waiting to go off duty to have the relief

31

still three miles down the road. I'd developed a reputation for creative alibis. Sometimes my colleagues made them up for me as I came skidding through the door. "Elephants clogging Seward Highway again, Leola?" "Out joyriding with Paul Newman in his new Porsche?"

On surgical duty, of course, lateness was simply unthinkable. Hence the classy alarm clock. I started days in surgery an hour ahead of schedule; on busy days, even earlier. That didn't endear me to everybody, either. Last week, a fellow nurse had said, "Leola, I swear you get scrubbed before sunrise!"

Today, thanks to the repair of my car, thanks to Bugler, I'd be right on the nose.

Memories. . . . To be treasured like fading snapshots, pasted in an album that I take out and look at once in a while. Nowhere among them can I find a clue, a hint of what was to come. For these were the last hours of the late great former Leola Harmon, a woman who was about to disappear. And they were all so ordinary.

CHAPTER 3

I opened my eyes in a blue-gray light. Dawn. More snow drifting silently by the window. For a moment I couldn't remember. Then I knew. I was in the recovery room, Intensive Care Unit. I knew the place well—better than I knew my own bedroom. For a moment I thought I was on duty, on the eleven-to-seven shift. I saw the suction machine on the bedside table. Then it occurred to me that I was observing things from an angle I'd never seen before. Sidewise. I was stretched out in the bed, my leg was immobile in a cylinder cast. *I was the patient.*

The impact exploded in my mind. What day is this? How badly banged up am I? I can see, through a blur to be sure, but I can see. Blurry vision is to be expected. I could raise my head slightly, move it from side to side. I did this cautiously, prepared for bad news. Relief. My neck was sore, bruised, but all the vertebrae still rotated. No spine damage here. I started curling my toes and worked my way upward, flexing every muscle I could flex. My knee sang out in pain. Broken kneecap. That would mean two months off work at least, maybe three. Otherwise everything was all right from the neck down.

I could feel no sensation at all between my throat, where I gingerly fingered the tracheotomy hole, and my eyes. I must have suffered some facial lacerations. I shuddered. My face! Oh God, will there be scars?

Somebody must have been a little too enthusiastic with the pain

33

killers. If this is the morning of the next day, and I think it is, I shouldn't be so socked in. There should be a nurse here. Where the heck is the nurse? *This* is Intensive Care? She's probably down the hall at the coffee machine, taking advantage because I'm staff. That's a good sign, it means they're not worrying about me. I'll give her a yell, let her know I know she's delinquent. Wonder who it is?

I didn't open my mouth to call. I couldn't—it was wired shut. Surprise, then a wave of alarm. What goes? I closed my eyes and rested, then slowly began to raise my hand toward my face. Someone caught my arm. It was the nurse. She had been there all the time, sitting so quietly I hadn't even noticed her.

"Don't touch," she said firmly, all professionalism. Now I was aware of all the tubes dangling above my head and shoulders. Strange that I had neither seen nor felt them. I must be fuzzier than I thought. One, two, three, four—*four* tubes? The whole artillery? I couldn't be this bad off! But somebody obviously thinks I am. I looked at the fast drip on the glucose. Apparently I had lost quite a lot of blood.

The nurse standing beside me was a virtual stranger. I vaguely remembered her as a transfer recently arrived from Edwards. Where were my buddies? What was going on? Later I was to learn that none of my friends on the nursing staff were permitted that day to visit or attend me. Daria had apparently tried, and been refused admittance.

"Hello, Lieutenant," the nurse said gently. "I'm Susan." She checked everything quietly, moving about in that special way nurses have when they're trying to be casual about something important.

I looked toward the door to my room, suddenly filled with the figure of a man who looked vaguely familiar. As he approached, I realized it was Dr. Stallings. He looked tired, but his "Good morning" was strong and confident.

A little early for rounds, I thought as he deftly checked the trach hole.

"I understand we have something in common, Lieutenant Harmon."

I just looked at him, wondering what that could be.

"Both workaholics. This looks just fine," he said more to himself

34

than to anyone else. "My name is Jim Stallings, we're going to be seeing quite a lot of each other from here on in. As you've probably figured out, I had to set your jaw fracture and have done some soft tissue work in your face."

Ah, I thought. I was right about the lacerations.

"Everything is under control. You've got some torn ligaments in that knee and of course it's going to be some time before you can speak again. I want you to take it easy, not fight anything. Okay?"

I blinked.

"Good. You need anything, let Susan know." He held up his hand as though anticipating my question. "You can write the requests. Now about your family . . ." He read the alarm in my eyes. "I understand that you don't want them to come, but we did have to let them know you were in an accident. I saw your husband last night after surgery, he's pretty rocky. I gather you two had an argument?"

I blinked again.

"He's taking this pretty hard."

Poor Gary, I thought. Probably feeling guilty. Well, no need for that now. We could begin again. Everything would be better than it had been before, I'd see to that.

When I opened my eyes, Stallings was gone. I must have drifted off. How rude. My eyes scanned the room for Susan. She was sitting in the chair, studying what appeared to be a textbook. I raised my hand and she immediately responded to the movement.

As Susan checked the rigging around my head, another nurse appeared in the door and asked her to step into the hall. I lay perfectly still, trying to hear what they were saying. No luck. Well, I'd find out soon enough. A moment later I heard her say, "Thank you."

I opened my eyes again and saw Susan approach the bed. "Your husband is here, shall I have him come in?"

I blinked, hard. She moved to the door and I heard her tell Gary he could only stay for a moment. He was wearing corduroys, a green flannel shirt, and a look of resolute concern. As he neared the bed, I thought he was about to say something ridiculous, like "Hello, how are you?" The words, whatever they might have been, never passed his lips. Nothing did. Not even a gasp. Shock, confusion, pain were stamped all over his face. My God, I thought, it must be bad. Worse than bad; he was staring at me in *revulsion*. He just hung there on his feet, immobile, mute. Then he wheeled and bolted for the door. I didn't need to be told he was vomiting up against the wall in the corridor. I could hear it. Susan sprang from the room. Good. He shouldn't be alone. *What was wrong with my face?* I struggled weakly and sank into unconsciousness.

The fugue, the confusion of the traumatically injured patient—there is no describing it. For the next 48 hours I floated in and out of pain, in and out of consciousness. When I was awake and rational I could scribble one- or two-word messages on a gray waxy slate. Children are given these "magic slates" as toys, but they were originally developed for laryngectomes, patients who have had surgery of the voice box, and for people like me with broken jaws. Shade up, plz. Plz, shade down. Plz wipe face . . .

Gary did not appear again. I thought about him—and his reaction. Could it have been the tubes, the wires in my jaw, the tracheotomy? Some men are squeamish about things like that. I thought about asking for him by writing his name on the slate. Once I even began with a *G*, a very elaborate Old English *G*, then stopped and abruptly lifted the covering sheet of plastic that instantly destroyed any writing.

At times there were staff members I knew hovering around my bed. None of them spoke directly to me. They spoke to each other, across me, and at times I would think, "Maybe I'm really dead. Why else would they act this way? As if I'm not even here." I began to pick up on little asides, one nurse murmuring to another, "In all my duty I've never . . ." and finishing the sentence with an inaudible whisper. Or: "I can't believe the way her husband is behaving . . ."

What was Gary doing, then? Getting drunk? Deserting the Air Force? Flaunting whores? None of these prospects seemed unlikely. Apparently he had gone off the deep end and, whatever the reason, could not bring himself to come back.

It followed, obscurely, that something must be wrong with me, something I hadn't been told. It bothered me, but I didn't try to figure it out. For the time being I was absorbed by pain in all of its varying degrees. Intermittent pain, unrelenting pain. Hours and hours of both.

While I don't recommend that every nurse get hit by a truck as part of her training, there is something to be said for spending some time on the other end of the chart. I learned some things about nursing care that I could not have learned any other way. Suction, for example. Give the patient time to get a deep breath of air before you push that tube down the trachea and start pumping. And don't stay down there so damned long. And the respirator: coordinate with the patient—don't explode my lungs with air while I'm still trying to exhale. Air. I vowed that if I ever got out of there I would stop complaining about the weather, I would leave every window wide open no matter what the temperature was and spend the rest of my life drinking in sweet, fresh air.

I had been in the hospital four days before the memory of my pregnancy penetrated the haze. I laboriously scrawled the question, "Baby?" Susan said she would get Dr. Gills if I wished. I blinked, a fervent "yes."

Dr. Gills was gentle; the baby had not survived. I imagined he could hear my silent, anguished cry. "I know, Leo, I know." And I knew that he did.

I searched his eyes for some clue about the loss of my baby. He simply stood by the side of the bed looking pale and tired. I was convinced there was something he wasn't telling me. Something horrible. I tried to beg him for a full report with my eyes. They felt raw from the strain. I lay there, one hysterical ex-mother, agony in her eyes and mind, her jaws wired shut, unable to speak to anyone but God. Maybe that's why people had been acting so strangely. Maybe that's what had made my husband flee the room. I remembered all those cruel words we, had exchanged that last night at home. It's all right, Gary, I understand. You didn't really mean it. People say terrible things out of fear.

Eventually, I read the medical report. The details are firmly imprinted in my mind. Nothing spectacular—a good, clean professional D&C. Lots of women have them. If there was an examination

37

to inquire whether the fetus had indeed died before the curette knife got to it, if the fetus was deformed, I do not know. I never tried to find out. The choice had not been mine. I concentrated my mind on a baby—whole, beautiful, healthy—in the arms of a loving and merciful God.

Daria was finally permitted to visit.

"At last!" she called out, bouncing in the door. She jerked a thumb at the startled—and always a little prim—nurse Susan and said, "Out in the hall. We want to tell dirty jokes." Susan fled.

"I heard you were up here, goofing off." She leaned over and kissed me twice on the forehead, then put her head down on my shoulder in among all the tubes, kissed me again and gave me a light, warm hug. Afterward I was to remember that she smiled, that she looked right at me—if not directly into my eyes.

She was patient with my inarticulate gurgles, some of which she even understood. With the aid of the slate and my growing repertoire of sounds, I was able to convey what I felt about the loss of the baby. She nodded solemnly, then bowed her head. Then she pointed at her own body, noticeably pregnant even beneath that boxy jacket. I knew she was in her fifth month. We had spent hours planning for our babies, promising to be godmothers to each other's children.

"We'll share this one for the time being." I knew she was being serious, not insensitive. As my eyes began to fill up with tears, I saw her own. "I mean it, Leo. I need you. You better not let me down." Before I could begin to scribble a protest on the slate she was off on a stream of merry, iconoclastic Air Force gossip. A major's wife had run off to Hawaii with a civilian hippie half her age. A pilot had gotten lost and headed for Archangel. Migs—Chinese or Soviet, the pilot wasn't sure—had risen to meet him and in perfect Winston Churchill English invited him to dinner. So embarrassing! A corpsman in ob-gyn had won a $50,000 lottery and given it all to Aleut orphans. Sober! I knew it couldn't have been Gary.

She said nothing about him, and she was gone before I could bring myself to ask. I was alone. Susan had apparently expected Daria to stay longer. I lay absolutely still, feeling vaguely disturbed. There had been something different about Daria's behavior. Not that *she* had been different. Her *visit* had been different in some way. What was it? Then I knew. Daris had looked at me. Other people looked past me, somehow, or looked at me without really focusing their eyes. I saw my husband in front of me again, horrified, repelled, sick.

I had not asked for a hand mirror to inspect the damage done to my face by the steering wheel, other parts of the car, the Alaskan snowscape. I knew full well that such inspection was discouraged in recovery rooms, even when the patients were medical personnel. My tongue felt as though it had been clamped in a hot waffle iron and was often in such pain that there was no sensation at all. I knew my teeth had done that job, and that I had probably broken or cracked my jawbone and lost some incisors. And yet, now, increasingly, I had the distinct impression that there was a lot more I didn't know.

I scanned the room. There was no mirror, but that was to be expected. Nor was there a picture with glass. Gauzy beige curtains let light in through my windows but covered the glass. Nothing could conceivably reflect my image. I was still alone. I had to know, whether they thought it wise or not. Feeling courageous and rather like a naughty child, I carefully disengaged all the tubes from my body and hung them back on their poles. "Susan isn't going to like this. Tough. I am sick and tired of all the pussyfooting around." I swung my cast-encased leg out of bed and dragged myself—limping, hobbling, clutching onto whatever I could find for support—ten excruciating feet to the bathroom. I leaned against the door frame gasping for breath, then turned on the light.

Below the eyes, most of what had been Leola Harmon's face was gone.

I blinked. It was no shadowy trick of lighting. There were few bandages, and the ones that were there concealed little. They seemed to taunt me: "You should see what's underneath!" I could just imagine. Flesh had been torn from my bones. Where were the missing sections of jaw? Strewn along Tudor Road? A few teeth, slanted crazily in my puffy gums, like you see on the aged among the very poor. The top half of my mouth was wrenched to one side in a horrible snarl. The right half of my lower lip down to the gum line seemed to be missing altogether. The left half was a mangled, bloody sponge—with missing strips—stitched up like a jigsaw puzzle. My eyes were still swollen; my heavy auburn hair had been chopped off and stood out around my head in ugly, inch-high tufts.

I once nursed a patient who had been attacked by a maniac with a meat axe, and another who had gone to the zoo and gotten too chummy with an alligator. Both had fared better than I had.

Swaying, my eyes closed but still able to see the ghastly image in the mirror, I prayed for death. "God, let me die. Just let me die. Now."

On my way back to the bed I stole a quick glance at my chart and discovered that I wasn't going to die. At least not physically. I was, in fact, doing quite well. Temperature, pulse, blood pressure, all vital signs encouraging. My leg wasn't even broken, I noted. Two deep gashes sutured; some damage to ligaments. I could hear some damned therapist wisecracking: "You'll be playing second base in a month." But my *face!* Gary had shouted that our baby would be a monster, and the baby was gone, and now here was mother-monster in its place.

Goodbye, Leola. It was an unspoken sob locked in my throat. Self-pity, how I had always loathed it in others. It washed over me in tidal waves. I kept staring at the chart. There was a hairline fracture but no notation of brain injury. I pulled myself back onto the bed and lay quietly, waiting for the spasms of pain and terror to subside. Okay, God. Since you intend for me to live, you might let me know your plans for me. To lose one's face is to lose one's self. The words hummed in my mind. What's behind the face—who's at home?

Then came the sickening realization: I didn't know.

CHAPTER 4

I opened my eyes; it was still true. I was alive, I was in the hospital. Judging by the light in the room it was late afternoon; I wondered where Susan was and then became aware of a presence next to the bed. I turned my eyes slowly, fully expecting to see Susan or one of the other nurses adjusting the rigging around my head. Instead, with a start, I saw an officer in full dress uniform standing beside the bed, his face obscured in the shadows. I wondered if many of them did that when I was unconscious or sleeping—stole in for a look at the horrifying mess that had once been Lieutenant Harmon.

A wave of anger ran through my body. It was Dr. Stallings! You! You saved my life, which makes you the one who did this to me! I studied him as intently as he did me. He leaned out of the shadows, seemingly oblivious to the hatred in my stare. *Trying to figure out what to do next?* The question would have been spoken with venom, if I could have spoken. Trying to figure out why you did it? What you saved me for? My God, even my own husband couldn't bear the sight of me.

Major Jim Stallings, all spit and polish—no doubt going out somewhere, something I would never be able to do—staring at me intently. I glared at him. Why are you looking at me like that? He was still oblivious to my stare. I was sure I was losing my mind: The expression on his face was as attentive as that of a man studying a particularly attractive woman. I had to be crazy. Yet it was true, there wasn't a trace of horror or pity anywhere in his expression.

His eyes finally caught mine and he smiled awkwardly, as if embarrassed at being surprised in an intense personal vision. He cleared his throat. "I hear your husband was here."

You're a master of understatement, I thought, still glaring.

"I'm sorry you had to be put through that, I'm sure he'll be all right in time."

I noticed that Stallings was holding a stack of medical reports; I assumed they were my history. He actually seemed cheerful. In fact, everything about him was positive, the way he stood, the directness of his eyes, the warmth of his smile. I felt a small tinge of hope in response to his overwhelming good humor.

"I guess you're getting impatient with all of this," he said drily.

"Right!" I scribbled furiously on the slate. He read the message and laughed, a slow, deep, easy laugh. A country boy, I guessed correctly.

Dr. Stallings pulled up a straight-backed chair and sat down beside my bed.

"Susan tells me you've been assessing the damage, Lieutenant."

I wondered what Susan had actually said; she had been shaken beyond belief and had given me hell while she reattached my IV tubes.

"There's no point in beating around the bush, Lieutenant, you're a pro and a damn good one from what everyone tells me. I've decided to review with you exactly what's happened. I know if I were you, I'd want to know."

I blinked my response enthusiastically.

"That's what I thought. I want you to read these reports so you'll know I'm not holding anything back. So far you have been through seven hours and fifteen minutes of non-stop surgery. Five doctors and four nurses on the job."

"Let me read it, plz."

By all rights, the report should have meant the end. Instead I now look upon it as an historic document. Because Jim Stallings happened to be at Elmendorf, I was on the threshhold of a challenging, miraculous endeavor. It sure didn't seem like it at the time.

Sometimes, even all these years later, I take that report out and scan the now familiar words. Morbid? I really don't think so—it

42

documents the beginning of the most extraordinary journey of my life. It has been an invaluable reminder, especially on those days when the mundane problems of living seem to be getting the upper hand. It has even helped others who have felt as hopeless about their own injuries as I once did about mine.

A tracheotomy was performed by Dr. Stallings. The patient was inducted with further anesthesia via the tracheotomy tube. The oral cavity was entered, revealing numerous fractured and avulsed teeth, and fragments of teeth. One metal tooth crown was removed from the pharynx. Deep lacerations of oral mucosa, avulsion of left tuberosity containing teeth #15, #16 into the left cheek. Fracture of the symphysis of the left mandible. Lower plate of the mandible free and attached only by lingual mucoperiosteum. There was a segment of bone containing teeth #24, 25, 26 which was dissected from the mucoperiosteum and removed. Jordan-Day drill in each of these segments, criss-cross wires 26-gauge stainless steel placed, bringing fragments into position. Lingual plate brought into apposition and one drill hole placed through lingual plate and one through buccal and wired. Mucoperiosteum closed with 3-0 black silk sutures. One Penrose drain placed in area. An Erich arch bar adapted to existing lower teeth and wired into position. A 24-gauge stainless steel wire was passed around the mandible over the arch bar and tightened into position. Circum zygomatic wires placed over right and left zygomatic arches by use of 18-gauge spinal needles. These wires brought into oral cavity in region of first molar teeth and twisted off into a loop configuration. Following this, one wire was placed through the loop on either side and through the arch bar and brought out and tightened, bringing the still existent upper teeth into apposition with the lower teeth. The patient seemed to tolerate the procedure well.

I paused, looking up at Dr. Stallings, and wrote on the slate, "Am I wired for sound?" My mouth had to look like the inside of a jungle gym. Just as well my tongue couldn't yet tell me about it. I had a feeling it would, though.

"Read on," Dr. Stallings urged. "The best part has yet to come."

Attention was then given to severe laceration of the lower lip. The laceration was through and through, dirty, jagged, with entire loss of some lip tissue. It was necessary to excise the unsuitable tissue. The lower lip was reconstructed by means of bilateral advancement flaps; a rotation flap from the skin of the chin and a double transposition or z-plasty at the mucocutaneous junction. The orbicularis oris muscle and mucosa closed with 3-0 catgut. Skin closed with 6-0 Tevdek. Unsuitable tissue discarded and dog ears from the flaps taken out in the usual fashion. Blood loss in operation estimated 300 cc's, blood loss prior, 700 cc's so 1000 cc's blood given. Immediate postoperative course excellent.

Dr. Stallings had done restorative plastic surgery in the course of emergency treatment! Highly unusual, to say the least. And hard work.

Considering what I had seen in the mirror, all his efforts had been wasted. My eyes stung.

Sunlight blazed off the brass on his meticulously pressed uniform as he bent over the bed to take my hands in his.

"Lieutenant, you may look like the bottom of hell now, but I swear to you, you won't always look this way. If you'll just give me time, I promise to make you entirely presentable. I can do the work, but you'll have to go along with me."

I felt electrified by his words, by the energy flowing from his hands into mine. I didn't take my eyes from him.

"Leola," his voice sang my name, "I'm talking about going along with I don't even know how many operations. If you have the guts, I have the time. And the skills. Will you trust me?" There wasn't the slightest trace of arrogance in his voice. I believed him.

Through what was left of my mouth, I got out a reasonable imitation of two words. "Yes, doctor."

He straightened. My hands were still in his. He placed them— gently, as though they were fragile—neatly on either side of my body. "Think about it. I know you can do it. What's important is that *you* know." He stood and absently adjusted his jacket. "I'll be going now. My wife is a pianist. She's in concert tonight. But I'll be here tomorrow and we'll talk again." His soft exit from the room made me remember the sonic boom of his entrance into the Emergency Room. God, how long ago was that?

44

He had called me by my first name. He had promised to make me entirely presentable. I wondered if it could be done; the extent of the injuries was so great. But could it be that the fact they were *my* injuries had colored my perception of them? God, I want to be out in the world again—I want life, I want it to be better than ever before!

Hold it. Don't get carried away. That's not what he promised. Besides, if he had said anything that extravagant, I would never have believed him. I knew better. He simply said *presentable*. If I could have, I would have smiled. Presentable. I had always been at least that, all my life. Dr. Stallings wasn't offering crumbs, he was offering an alternative. One that I didn't have an hour ago. I closed my eyes and allowed sleep to separate me from the anguish that had become my constant companion.

Daria noticed the change in me. "You seem much perkier today. Feeling better?"

I nodded, scribbled "Dr. S. was here."

She grinned. "He's been pretty verbal about his good prognosis for you. But you knew that already, didn't you?"

I wrote, "Not till now."

"They say he's truly extraordinary. Trust him, Leo. I don't think he's the type to smarm a patient with a bedside manner."

"I do," I wrote.

"Brought you your mail. There's one from home and one from Motor Vehicles. You want me to read them to you?"

"No. Do it later mysf."

"You always were independent. Stubborn too, thank God."

I wanted to ask her about Gary, if she had talked to him, if she had any idea what was going on. . . . Later, I'd ask her later. Right now I wanted to keep on absorbing Stallings' good news.

I was still adamant about not letting my family know the extent of my injuries. The staff had gone along, against their better judgment. The letter from my stepmother was cheery and consoling about the loss of the car; all she had been told was that I had been in an accident which totaled the Mustang. She offered to help me buy another car. She would have to be told the truth eventually, of course. At the moment I was glad that some instinct had made me hold back. If

45

Stallings was right, it would be easier for my family to deal with my injuries at a point when they could be told there was *some* hope.

I opened the envelope from the Alaska Department of Motor Vehicles and gurgled. "Your failure to file report of accident of November 8 within 10 days is a violation of the law. Your driver's license is suspended." That isn't all that's been suspended, I thought.

The next day I asked Dr. Stallings if I might take over my own care. He reacted with such obvious pleasure that I knew it was the right thing to do. More than anything, it told him that I was willing to work with him and wanted to get started.

"I think that's a marvelous idea."

My last intravenous tube removed—this time under supervision—and I demonstrated to everyone's satisfaction that I could manipulate the remaining I.V. with considerable skill. I took over my trach care and was meticulous with the Water Pik, which was vital to my oral hygiene. I still had to have tube feedings, dining on pulverized slush. But my blood cell count was back to normal and I began to believe the day would come when I'd be able to eat real food again. A walking cast was made for my knee and, with a crutch, I could get around.

I felt a sense of freedom out of all proportion to the circumstances. It meant so much to be mobile again, to be self-sufficient, not to lie in bed in passive pain. There was still pain, but I could not tell myself that it was the pain of growth, of healing, that one day it too would pass. My being active also made it possible to endure the downcast eyes, the stares that seemed focused at a point somewhere above my head. It would take time for the horror of my face to be corrected, I knew that. But perhaps with time and hard work, people would look at me without cringing. With the exception of Daria and Dr. Stallings, my fellow staffers all projected a reaction that I found simply unbearable: pure, unadulterated pity—a reaction I could not handle and was determined to change.

The more I did for myself, the more stimulated I became. I was getting caught up in the experience of being on the patient's side in a very difficult situation. I began to experiment with varying ways of suctioning myself—the trach had to be unclogged regularly as a precaution against pneumonia. I learned to take a deep breath, brace myself, go down, suction and come out, feeling comfortable and easy. What was to prevent all trach patients from learning this—or, at least, developing a set of signals to enable the nurse to work with and not against them? My mind was filled with ideas, ideas that replaced the nagging question: Where was Gary? Maybe Daria would phone him for me. Maybe she already had and hadn't been able to bring herself to tell me what was going on. After all, I hadn't been able to bring myself to ask her about him.

I began to think that I might be back on the job soon. My optimism on this score would evaporate whenever I thought about my face. They'd never dare put me back to work. One look would send any patient into instant relapse. At best I could probably look forward to spending the rest of my life buried in some back lab. For although the swelling had begun to diminish, what faced me in the bathroom mirror was still hard to take. It still took me a few seconds to get over the shock every time I looked. How could I blame other people? The huge, hurt, angry brown eyes reflected my inner turmoil. At least *they* hadn't been damaged.

Dr. Stallings didn't return for nearly a week. It seemed like a month. Was he having second thoughts? If he was, I didn't want to know it. Not now, not after making so much progress. I tried to shake off these doubts just as I struggled to shake off mental pictures of my face as it was now—or wasn't. He had made me a solemn promise. He would keep it.

Gary arrived, with flowers, and was immediately told they were not permitted in Intensive Care. He knew. He didn't think. He was clearly miserable and there under duress. I didn't know which was worse, seeing him, not seeing him. He arrived again, this time bearing candy. How the hell did he think I could eat chocolate creams through a feeding tube? Or taste them? As furious as I was, I also realized he was really rattled.

I drew a bravely smiling cartoon face, meant to be myself, added piles of fluffy new hair and wrote, "Soon," beneath it. I showed it to him, then destroyed the upbeat picture and wrote, "I'll be fine. Stay home. Study. Don't worry."

"You mean you don't want me to come here?"

"Right," I scribbled. "Upsetting for both."

"Are you sure?"

I nodded. I was sure. I was also annoyed by the relief that illuminated his face. A few minutes later, he was gone.

Daria must have been coming up on the elevator as Gary was going down. She barged into the room and flung her arms up in the air. Then she began to dance around, shadow boxing. I looked at her in mild astonishment.

"There's a shouting match you wouldn't believe going on over at Headquarters." She sat in the chair and removed her cap. "All about you, I might add. Your doctor, Major Stallings, is taking the place apart!"

I drew a big question mark on the slate.

"Sergeant Jones, the general's secretary, told Bob all about it and he called me. Of course Bob promised he wouldn't breathe a word, but he figured it was okay to tell me." She chuckled. "Wait'll you hear!"

A smile welled up inside me. Wonderful, irrepressible Daria.

"It seems Dr. Stallings went in to talk to the colonel about a series of operations he wants to schedule for you. The colonel was very enthusiastic and began to make the arrangements—he got out his calendar and they started ticking off dates, assigning staff, making requisition lists. Then all of a sudden the colonel takes another look at your records and shakes his head. Sorry, Major. No way. Seems your enlistment is about up, Leo—well, we knew that—and in spring you'll be a civilian again. No room for you in a military hospital, with a military surgeon, under those circumstances. Time for one teeny operation, maybe."

I felt numb.

Daria waved her hand, reading my thought in my eyes. "Hang on, I'm not done yet. Dr. Stallings goes charging over to Headquarters and tackles the general. 'Extend her enlistment!' The general says no. The general also says impossible. Contra-policy. Now Stallings is pounding the desk. 'Lieutenant Harmon will never be able to afford reconstructive surgery if she's a civilian. It could run into hundreds of thousands of dollars. There are few surgeons who would undertake such new procedures for any amount of money. General, you can't do that!' " Daria closed her eyes. "Leo you *know* a major does not tell a general 'You can't do that.' Sergeant Jones said he expected the general to have a stroke, or at the very least to have Dr. Stallings lined up and shot. Instead the sergeant hears the general saying, 'Okay, okay.' The next thing he knows, the general is writing. Leo, you're in the Air Force for two more years and Stallings has a go-ahead on his plans for you!" Daria's eyes were shining. I knew mine were too.

The next day Dr. Stallings strode in, smiling. "Big secret," he said, putting a finger to his lips. "I don't want you to even scribble a syllable. Just listen. I was able to have your enlistment renewed so we could operate. Keep your slate quiet until everything is final, it still has to go through channels. You will re-enlist, won't you?"

I nodded.

"Okay, let's get to work." He pulled some X rays from a manila envelope he had brought along and we reviewed the state of my jaw bones, cheek bones, teeth. Then he pulled from his pocket a small sketch pad. He drew a surprisingly good likeness of me as I once had been, although he did put a dimple in I'd never had.

"Here's what we're going to do," he said as he marked up the image. Oral surgery, the first operation he had planned, would be the roughest, the longest and the worst. "If you're still speaking to me after that, the rest won't be quite so traumatic."

"Hw mny ops in all?"

He looked at me for a long moment. I knew he was weighing the answer carefully, deciding if he should risk the truth or just offer up generalities. He opted for truth. "Hard to tell, Leo. Perhaps as many as forty."

Leo, he called me Leo. Forty operations? No one could possibly be that important!

But a look at the surgeon sitting beside my bed assured me that he was in absolute earnest. This man had already risked so much: shoving a fellow officer in the E.R., yelling at a general on my behalf. Who was I to question his resolution?

He took my hand. "We'll be partners, Leo, in an adventure for

49

which I have high hopes. It will work out well, I know it will. The degree of our success will depend on some factors we can't control, like Lady Luck and God, not necessarily in that order."

The psychic magic he projected infused me with such hope, I recognized myself zapping along on the high that only the most confident, trusting patient can feel.

"Tell me about yrslf."

"You really want to know?" He seemed pleased.

I nodded and scribbled, "You know all about me. Only fair. Especially if we're going to be partners."

He leaned back in the chair, stretched out his legs and put his arms behind his head. "What's a former ENT specialist like me doing remodeling a woman's face? Good question. The answer is, I'm in love—really in love with the thrill, the joy of plastic surgery. Restorative, reconstructive, functional, cosmetic—the whole bag. I first realized it when, as an ear, nose and throat man, I became involved in attempts to reconstruct for cancer patients who had laryngectomies. There they were, stuck with mechanical squawk boxes for the rest of their lives. Why not build a new larynx? By the time I reached the end of my residency, I was hooked and doing only throat whenever I could manage it."

"Lucky for me," I wrote.

"You're right, you wouldn't be here now if I hadn't become so attuned to the sounds of the trachea in acute distress. You would have survived that horrendous accident only to be done in by a blob of gold in your windpipe. Somehow, I don't think that would have made sense. I heard you strangling right through the swinging door."

"And I heard you roar!"

"I learned the art of bellowing from cows."

"COWS?" I printed.

"Growing up on a small dairy farm. Near Marion, Arkansas, just across the Mississippi River from Memphis." He held up his hands. "I got these strong fingers from milking seven cows morning and night. My father added to the family income by taking the job of town jailer. I was the only kid around with a real six-shooter to play with. Two winters, when times were really hard, we lived above the

50

jail. Then we moved to Pomatok, Mississippi. I had an older cousin, Jim, who was a doctor in general practice in Oxford. When I was fourteen, Cousin Jim let me come into the operating room, all scrubbed and gowned, and witness surgery. Removal of a diseased ovary. And that was what decided me—from then on I knew I would be a doctor, a surgeon."

He stopped. "I'm talking your ear off and then I'll have to replace *that*."

"No. Go on, plz."

"I got through college in three years with a double major, zoology and chemistry. Worked as a dishwasher in the college cafeteria. I met a girl, a music student, four years older than me. We married. I did two years of medical school at the University of Mississippi and transferred to the University of Pennsylvania for my internship. Next came two years of general surgery at the University of Iowa, a year of practicing medicine at Mercy Hospital in Mason City and three years of ear, nose, and throat at the University of Iowa. I was certified in ENT in 1968 and the local draft board beckoned. I signed up right away for the Air Force and that's how I got to Elmendorf. There you have it, the life and times of Jim Stallings."

I asked him by way of a carefully printed line on the slate if I might take over all of my own nursing care.

"You've been doing a lot of it anyway, from what I hear. I'll say yes—on one condition."

I looked at him eagerly.

"If it turns out to be too much, you don't tough it out. You let me know."

I scribbled, "That's a promise!"

For the next two weeks, except for the eight hours a night I slept, I attended to all of my own needs rather than the few that had been delegated so reluctantly. And while my own care required meticulous attention, it still wasn't enough to keep me occupied. I began to catch myself brooding over what lay ahead. The future, once so bright and full of promise, now stretched ahead of me like a flat, gray plain. The now-familiar sight of my face in the bathroom mirror was indelibly stamped in my mind. All my life I had taken my looks for granted—had, in fact, gotten by on them. Now they were gone. The Leola who looked that way had been left somewhere on Tudor Road. And while I can't say that I wanted to die, I wasn't entirely sure that I wanted to live. My bravado was beginning to wear thin; I needed something else to occupy my mind. I asked Captain Laura if I might take over the care of three other patients in the unit. She almost blew a gasket.

"Are you mad, Lieutenant? Think of all the blood you lost!"

"I *will* go mad if I can't keep occupied!" I wrote.

She looked at me thoughtfully. I could feel her trying to imagine what it must be like to be the sort of prisoner I had become. I knew she fully understood the importance of my need to be useful.

"All right," she said finally. "I guess you've had us buffaloed with all that endless good cheer you've been exuding."

"Hysteria," I wrote.

"In any other patient we would have recognized it as such."

"No matter," I wrote.

"If Dr. Stallings approves, I certainly won't stand in your way. I'll ask him to step in and see you as soon as he can."

I nodded, too grateful to scribble a line.

After giving me a thorough going-over, Stallings announced that he could find no medical reason to refuse my request.

"I'm assuming you won't neglect your own care," he said.

I shook my head.

"I believe you. You know, most patients who've gone through what you have would still be lying in bed, doped up, complaining. You amaze me."

I shivered with delight at the compliment. I had a feeling that patients didn't amaze him too often.

The work in the unit went well and acted like a tonic on my spirits. With each small accomplishment, I felt stronger and spent less time contemplating any future less immediate than, say, the next day.

Dr. Stallings announced finally that the date for the first operation had been determined. "February 10."

That was two months away. "Good," I wrote. "Now I go home."

"Now you're asking too much." He was annoyed.

I shook my head and pointed to the words on the slate. Then, with great care, I began writing down all of the logical reasons I should be allowed to leave the hospital.

He studied them, phrase by phrase, then handed the slate back to me.

"Level with me, Leo. I can't possibly release you unless I know what's on your mind."

A grunt? A sigh? A gurgle? Some sound that defies description came out of my throat. I wrote five words: "Husband. Love. Think over surgery."

"I see. You want to be at home with your husband, that's understandable. But are you trying to tell me you're having second thoughts about surgery?" He seemed genuinely baffled. I could see the unphrased question in his eyes. How could I not want to be at least presentable?

"Rt!"

He shook his head. "I can give you a million legitimate reasons why going home is inadvisable. But you've been right about everything you've wanted to do so far, I suppose it wouldn't hurt for you to get out for a while. All right. Go on home. And if you do change your mind about the surgery, I can always cancel your re-enlistment."

I scribbled quickly, "Don't do that. I love the Air Force!" He laughed in spite of himself.

I began to pack. There weren't many items. No one had thought to order me a new uniform to replace the soiled and blood-stained one that had been cut off my body. I was going home in a plain dark sweater and wraparound skirt that covered most of my cast. I had asked Daria to pick the outfit up for me, since Gary was adhering to my request that he not visit any more. Now I had to put on one lined boot. Just getting the sock on had worn me out. Maybe Stallings was right, maybe I was making a mistake. But I had to go home. I had to resolve the situation with Gary. I carefully wrote the apartment phone number on the slate and the words, "Tell my husband to come get me. Am being released." I carried the slate to the nurses' station and handed it to a startled Susan.

I was suddenly aware that my heart was pounding slowly but

strongly. Laboring. And my breath—there wasn't enough air. Susan, her back to me, began to dial the number. I stretched out my hand. It was trembling.

I knew perfectly well there was nothing wrong with my air supply, not any more. And never with my heart. I was having an anxiety attack! People had asked at different intervals if I were subject to them; every time I had scribbled the same answer on the slate, "Lord, no." Now I was experiencing a lulu. I knew that such attacks were powerful enough to knock you over, so I leaned on the counter that separated me from Susan.

Dear God, I know this must be happening because I'm so afraid. I don't know what's waiting for me with Gary, with myself, with all of these operations. I asked you to show me the way, well, now's the time. I need help.

I looked up. Dr. Stallings was stepping out of the elevator. "Leo, I don't want you to leave, not yet. Come back to the room and we'll talk."

Susan turned to face us. "I just spoke with your husband, Leola. He said he'd start out right away."

I nodded, but allowed Dr. Stallings to walk back to the room with me. I eased myself onto the bed and he faced me in the chair.

"Leola, you can't leave here." His words tumbled out in a passionate rush. "You can't be serious about having second thoughts. Maybe I was too honest about what restoring your face is going to involve. I wish you could see what I see. I *know* this has been an ordeal, I know how much lies ahead. But what you experience out there," he stopped to draw a breath, "may undo all the tremendous progress you've made. God saved your life. That accident brought us together so that something good can come out of this terrible experience. Let it happen, Leo." He was talking as though his life, not mine, depended on my remaining in the hospital. "You haven't been destroyed, you're still you.

"All the strongest, all the finest parts of your nature will come forward and grow stronger as you make your way through what's ahead. When it's over with, you'll not only feel better, you'll be a better person than you ever were before. You'll be happier, more whole. And when we show what we can do together, other wounded and injured people may even take heart and say, 'I can do that, too.' They'll see your light shining through a wonderful, new package— people do come in packages, Leo. I'll make one that's fully worthy of you."

The rush of words finally stopped. I was stunned. The man's intellectual and emotional commitment to restoring my face were simply overpowering. Why me? For the first time since the accident the question wasn't posed with rage, but with a sense of wonderment. What sort of an M.D. was this? What sort of man?

Now he was holding me by the shoulders and staring directly into my mutilated face.

"I can do it, Leo. But you have to cooperate, you have to want what I have to give. We can do it. You must believe that!"

He dropped his arms to his sides. I extended my hand and he offered me his. We shook hands firmly without any words. *I have just made the strongest pledge I would ever make in my life.* I felt strangely free.

Dr. Stallings looked at the door and my eyes followed his gaze. Captain Laura was standing in the doorway, disapproval written all over her face. "Your husband is waiting downstairs, Lieutenant." She glared at Stallings, no doubt wondering why he had permitted me even to think of leaving. Then she saluted and disappeared into the corridor.

"I'll help you down, even though I know I'm going to regret it."

I reached for the slate. "Hve to do this."

He nodded.

One day, when I could speak again, I would explain.

CHAPTER 5

In a borrowed car, Gary drove me to Seward Avenue through roads and streets piled with fortresslike banks of snow. The walls were plugged with great chunks of ice, stained with splashes of oil and grime. The frozen wastes of the Far North, the earthquake and tidal wave scars, the awkward housing thrown up on stilts . . . it was as if I were seeing them for the very first time.

It struck me that few of us had anything here other than a temporary, even reckless sense of living. Work, make money, blow it; then shake Alaska off your shoes and go home. Everywhere I looked there were my countrymen, but this wasn't their country. It showed in the way they lived, spoke, and behaved.

"Want to stop here?" Gary asked, slowing at a shopping center.

I raised my eyebrows.

"We have to get a blender so you can eat. At least, that's what they told me at the hospital."

I nodded. He parked the car and I stepped shakily out of the car. This being my first public appearance, I wasn't sure I could handle the reactions my face was sure to get. We entered a hardware store—and no one reacted. I couldn't believe it. But it was the week before Christmas, and the holiday crowds seemed oblivious of anything other than shopping.

The salesman who finally waited on us hardly seemed to notice my appearance. After several attempts to engage me in a dialogue about the various models the store stocked, I pointed to the wire in my jaws. This didn't faze him. "How about this one? Five speeds, $29.99? It's really a good buy, lady."

"*Lady?*" Well that certainly beat being called "it." I nodded to Gary and we bought the machine, refusing the offer for gift wrap.

The apartment house on Seward Avenue was a casually constructed two-story "Alpine." We were on the second floor, reached by a wooden staircase leading to a veranda that ran the length of the building. Ours was the second unit, off the north corner. I faced the stairs with some trepidation but made my way up, Gary carrying the blender ahead of me. I stood on the veranda and caught my breath, more or less smiling at my successful climb. Home, at last! How I had missed it during all those long, lonely weeks. Gary bounded down the steps and came back up with my bag and a kit of post-surgical maintenance equipment. It contained everything I might need from hemostats to tranquilizers.

He suggested I get out his key and open the door. He balanced the load in his arms against the wall of the building; I reached into his right pocket and fumbled through some loose change until I found the key. I opened the door and walked in.

There must be some mistake. This isn't where I live. Stale beer fumes. Dirty bath towels looped over chairs. The sink piled high with dirty pots and scummy dishes. On the floor, aluminum and paper junk-food receptacles. Overflowing waste baskets. All of my plants dead.

I stumbled and caught myself on the frame of the door leading into my kitchen, the kitchen I had left in such apple-pie order.

"I came as soon as the hospital called," Gary said from behind me. "Kind of a mess, I know. Sorry I didn't have a chance to clean up . . ."

Very slowly, I hobbled on to the living room. The smell of old smoke and booze made me choke. Ashtrays overflowed onto the tables; even the beer cans were stuffed with butts. In the bedroom I was greeted by a tangle of dingy, rumpled sheets, stained blankets, soiled underwear in random heaps.

A wave of anger rose in me and became a rage so terrible I had to speak! "Zis hum? Hat kin fmly du cm fum . . ." *This is my home?*

What kind of family do you come from? I raised my arm and swept it forward: "G-g-g-g"

Gary knew it meant go. He scrambled, clutching up trash as he went. I must have looked wild, with my hands flailing, eyes blazing in my livid red face. I reeled to the closet, pulled out a broom and sponge mop.

I swept and sponged in a kind of frenzy. Roaches darted from under the sink. I swung the broom like an avenger, dragging my cast—thump! thump!—behind me.

Twenty minutes later Daria and Bob arrived carrying a large, piping-hot pizza.

"I know you two like the expensive gourmet stuff," Daria announced as she plopped the carton down on the kitchen table that now reeked of ammonia. "Anchovies on one half, mushrooms on the other. You can't taste it, Leo, but you can smell it and that's half the fun." She lifted the disc from the box and displayed it proudly. "Ever see a blender pizza? Watch this!" I noticed the subtle kick she aimed at Bob who, thus prodded, took up an armload of bundled trash that still awaited transport.

Gary looked at Daria. "You didn't by any chance bring some beer, did you?"

Daria shot him a glance that would have shrivelled a lesser man. "No. I know you always have it on hand."

Her sarcasm eluded Gary. "We're clean out. I need some cigarettes anyway, I'll just be a few minutes." He slipped on his parka and stepped out the kitchen door.

"I'll go with him," said Bob.

"Good idea," said Daria. As soon as the door closed she turned to me. "How could he do this?"

I shrugged.

"Well, park yourself for a minute and rest. Let me get some of this cleared up. All you have to do is write directions, whereabouts of mop, cleansers, all that."

I slumped into a chair while Daria rummaged through my bag and pulled out the slate.

Two hours later, Bob returned. Daria was mopping the floor and I

59

was polishing the front windows. They were coated with a greasy film. The pizza lay cold on the table.

"Where's Gary?" Daria asked as Bob closed the door quietly.

"He ran into a friend," said Bob. "He's very concerned about you, Leo. He's staying with his friend until he calms down."

I didn't believe a word of it. Gary was probably with a friend all right, the kind that comes in an amber bottle.

Daria looked at me, then at the pizza; picked it up and placed in back in the carton. "I have a feeling we should try something a little easier to digest." She rummaged in the refrigerator, got out some eggs and milk and proceeded to whip me up a tasty eggnog which I sipped while she scrambled eggs for herself and Bob.

Daria helped me into bed while Bob made several more trips down the stairs with trash. "I know it's a hell of a homecoming, Leo. Obviously he hasn't been able to cope."

I just nodded. Before the accident, if Gary drank in a bar beyond my interest or tolerance, I would simply get up and leave. Eventually some buddy always deposited him on the doorstep in the early hours. I never did find out exactly where he had gone that night. At about two A.M., Bob apparently located him, just as the local police and the M.P.s were about to converge on him in the street.

When Gary drank, he sometimes became completely helpless. His sweet-natured chatter had made him a favorite at the bar, but sometimes he would get so stoned that he would have to be helped home.

Apparently Bob drove him around in the MG and tried to sober him up while Daria finished cleaning the apartment. I have no memory of her leaving, so I must have just drifted off to sleep.

In the morning I faced the shiny new blender, more or less ready to cope with the process of ingesting nourishment. A tube-fed patient in the hospital usually keeps the tube in, once it has been put in place. But at home, leading a quasi-normal life, I had decided against trying to move around with a tube swinging about my battered face and shoulders. I intended to re-insert it at each meal.

I had become quite proficient at getting the tube in without gagging or retching during my practice runs in the hospital, and it was no different that first morning at home.

The biggest problem was going to be finding something to puree, since Gary had obviously not given much thought to marketing. Daria had left a note on the kitchen table saying she'd be by with groceries before going to work. For the moment, I would have to make do with whatever was on hand. I cooked up some bran cereal, coddled an egg and placed both in the blender with half a cup of milk. I placed the lid on the glass container and pushed the button. The blender whirred nicely and I raised the lid to check the consistency. The bran was lumpy. I gave it another whirr—and the tube' dangling from my nose caught in the maelstrom of bran, egg and milk. I fell back as the tube was snatched out of my throat, knocking the blender off the counter. It was still churning madly, spraying my first homemade meal all over my clothes, the floor, the walls. I reached out and yanked the plug from the wall, skidded on what was to have been breakfast and hit the floor.

I sat in the middle of the mess and cried. The first tears I had shed in I didn't know how long. Certainly the first since the accident. My pride was hurt more than anything else; my cast was still intact and so was the tube. I slowly pulled myself to my feet, gathered everything up and put it in the sink, and began mopping up the mess. I wiped the blender base, rinsed the container, set the tube aside. Put that in last. Puree first, then put in the tube. I should have realized that to begin with. This time everything worked perfectly and I "ate" quietly. Tears of relief stung my eyes and the raw flesh. A good all-out cry was what I needed more than anything, but I couldn't yet. At least I felt a little better; some of the tension was gone.

Because my jaw was wired shut, a telephone code had been arranged if I needed to call for help—a simple S.O.S. signal tapped into the direct line in Dr. Stallings' office. But you can't very well call a doctor who might send a Medical Corps emergency crew across the mountain when your hungover husband comes home and buries his head in your lap, crying. Or when you have your third ludicrous accident of the day as you're trying to deal with simple household chores.

"Gary get help, get some counseling, you can't handle this

alone." I was to write such messages more than once on the slate. The answer was always the same. He would. He was sorry. He would stop drinking.

I arranged to collect the insurance on the car and sent Gary out to buy a new one.

I tried to encourage sexual intercourse and found my husband willing but impotent. I turned on the bedside light and wrote that it was all right, that I understood. Which I did.

The days passed more smoothly, the apartment was clean and comfortable. Gary seemed calmer, less ready to escape the sight of me by heading for the nearest bar.

A court date had been set for the insurance hearing. I wrote to the attorney for my insurance company and explained why I couldn't give testimony. He wrote back and said to come anyway, my wired jaws would help our case.

It was of course not a jury trial, just a traffic court hearing for drunken driving. Daria couldn't come, but Bob picked me up and stayed with me throughout. Gary had asked to be excused on the grounds that he might make a scene.

I was finally able to get a good long look at the man who had done this to me. In his forties, he had a furrowed face, sagging belly, a genuinely bewildered look in his eyes; it was established that when he had been checked in at the Eskimo he had a breath analysis of .05. Quite a load for early afternoon. His attorney explained that his client drove night shifts, that he was on his way home after making a delivery of vital mining equipment, that he needed to take amphetamines to stay awake on the road so Alaska could progress. Nezedrine, a recognized, respectable drug prescribed by the man's physician, was said to have inpaired his driving. Distance and space perception distorted by bennies.

I snorted, loudly. To my surprise, I heard a salvo of approving noises from the gallery. The judge, who hadn't been looking my way, banged the gavel and demanded "Order."

The assistant prosecuting attorney handling my case knew that the untoward display of support could hardly help. The judge didn't like this sort of thing.

Trying desperately to maintain my professional calm, I watched the truck driver. I am a nurse; that's the proudest fact of my life. That man is a drunk; he's ill, he needs help. I could smell him in the ambulance before my windpipe began to close. Look at him. A medical case. Get out the Librium.

The judge fined the truck driver $250. It was his first offense. His license was suspended for thirty days and he was sentenced to jail for the same amount of time.

The defense attorney pleaded for his client. "Your Honor, this man has a family to support. He has two children. I ask you to suspend sentence, for his children's sake."

"So ordered." The gavel banged. "Remanded to Parole Division."

I was on my feet, my hideous red face in plain view of anyone who cared to look at it.

Bob touched my arm. "Rotten deal, Leo. Come on, honey. Let's go home."

I turned, glared at Bob, and managed a garbled protest: "Sake hs chdrin? Wha bow my chld? My babby?"

Gary did take my advice and go for counseling. His therapist, an overburdened psychiatric social worker, came to see me. He seemed to have no trouble communicating hard facts.

"Your husband is having a very difficult time adjusting to your injury."

Scribble, "I know."

"It is an injury that is as severe to him as it is to you."

Scribble, "Yes."

"He sees your recovery as very far away. Like a mirage in the distance."

I nodded.

"He's determined to act as though nothing at all has happened. For the time being, try to go on as usual."

"Do you think my injury is all there is to the problem?" I wrote.

The therapist rose and put out his hand. "I'm glad we had this opportunity to talk, Mrs. Cox."

I never knew where all the hatred that boiled within me during those weeks came from. It gave me some understanding for those monsters of fiction who rage around, destroying all who quail at their sight. Gary indeed wanted to "go on as usual," which translated as pub crawling. I was out of my cast by now, walking with a slight limp, but my leg was otherwise as good as ever. I took perverse pride in dressing well. I wore sheer hose and pretty leather pumps whenever I didn't have to walk through snow. I bought a pair of jade and pearl earrings.

The ends of my sheared-off hair were stiff and mouse-colored; there was no way to cut or shape it. I bought a wig. My body was in good condition thanks to the carefully measured, nutritious food I was whipping up in the blender. I bought a down-filled coat that swung about my calves like the wrap of some arrogant empress.

I steeled myself to face the world and went out with Gary. Oddly enough, the more expensive places were the worst. Perhaps the fact that there were fewer customers made me stand out more. I began to take for granted the *maitre d*'s startled glance, the quick escort to a secluded table where I'd be least likely to be noticed by the other patrons. And, always, the agonized look in Gary's eyes, so at variance with his casual pose.

"Why in the world do you go out with him?" Daria demanded. "You can't eat. You can't drink. You can't even talk."

"Beats staying home alone," I wrote.

"I'm not sure," she said. "I mean, I can see getting out to see a movie, or visiting with friends. But to put yourself through this sort of torture seems crazy. And why does *he* do it?"

"Trying to be helpful," I scrawled.

Daria finished stacking the canned goods she had brought from the market. "Sounds to me like he's trying to martyr himself. Brings you out in public when you're really not ready. It's almost as if he's saying, 'Look, everyone. Here's that knockout you used to see me with. Look at her now and aren't I noble and wonderful, acting as though nothing's wrong.' I'm sorry, Leo, but it doesn't strike me as considerate at all."

I avoided her eyes. The same thought had crossed my mind more than once.

"Why don't you tell Stallings about this, next time you see him? It can't be doing much for your morale."

64

She was right about that, for sure. Again and again the trained nurse in me did battle with the humiliated female. I recognized Gary's agony, I saw his struggle to act as if everything was going to be all right, I even—sometimes—felt tenderness for him. At other times I wanted to claw at his pretty face.

I took Daria's advice and talked to Stallings, not specifically about Gary but about people's reaction to me in general.

"I can't tell you what to do with your personal life, Leo. I can make the observation that hauling around to bars and restaurants doesn't make sense right now. You're making impossible demands on yourself and others every time you do. It really isn't necessary to put yourself through that sort of pain. What's important is that you not let *anything* come between you and your recovery. What you can't handle, whom you can't handle, put aside for now. Shelve it. What you and I are about to do together matters more than anything. You have to hold yourself steady and stop trying to prove your mettle. I *know* you've got what it takes. Now you must start believing it—and how can you, while you're putting yourself on public display? Of course people are going to react. They don't know you aren't going to be disfigured for life."

I nodded slowly, "I'll try," I wrote, "to believe."

Dr. Stallings had become the only island of sanity in my life. He had a way of lifting me up, making me feel that I really did have whatever resources were needed for the ordeal that lay ahead.

We met frequently. In his sketchbook, he made drawings of each step he was planning to take. At his request I had sent home for childhood photographs which he had studied carefully, analyzing every phase of my facial development.

I asked once if he or any other plastic surgeon could make me look like Sophia Loren or Faye Dunaway. Or could he take them and make them look like someone else?

I expected an answer as facetious as my question. But Dr. Stallings said, very seriously, "I am not about to give you a completely different face, Lieutenant. A plastic surgeon can never be God, no matter how great his skills. All we can do is be a servant and do our best to put right what time and circumstances have put wrong."

He told me about Tagliozzi, the first doctor in history to try plastic surgery. "Did you know that in the sixteenth century Tagliozzi did nose jobs? Of course, he only repaired and whittled down noses. But he was the one who thought up the idea of borrowing skin from the upper inner arm, because that part of the arm has skin similar to that of the nose."

I knew that a plastic surgeon couldn't use just any old piece of skin, that it not only had to come from the patient but also had to be similar to the skin being replaced. It had never occurred to me to wonder who had been the first to use this procedure that would have such a profound effect on my own life.

"Tagliozzi figured out a way to bind the arm to the newly sculpted nose until the skin had healed." Stallings told me. "Then he would cut the two apart. The same procedure is still used for some rhinoplasty today. He earned fame and riches in his lifetime, but after he died, there were those who said he had interfered with God's work. His body was removed from hallowed ground and planted in a field somewhere. But look what he started, Leo!"

The story had all the elements of a fairy tale, but I wrote parts of it down carefully. I particularly liked Tagliozzi's statement of intent: *To restore, repair, even beautify all those parts of the body which nature has given but misfortune has taken away—not so much for the sake of life beyond but that they may buoy the spirit and help life on earth.*

I showed the notes I had taken to Gary, who read them carefully. I waited expectantly for some word of encouragement; none was forthcoming. While I believed the therapist's assertion that Gary had been deeply traumatized by the accident, I couldn't help wondering how much Gary was telling him in their sessions. Did the therapist know that Gary's attitudes and behavior predated the accident? I had the feeling that he did not, that the therapist himself was a little traumatized by my injuries. Why else would he have dismissed me? Never asked to meet with me again? On the other hand, maybe that was normal. *Keep steady.* I gave myself the advice Dr. Stallings had given me. *Stop wasting your time trying to get inside Gary's mind, the only person you can change is yourself.* I added some encouragement of my own. *How can you miss with a man like Dr. Stallings? He has already buoyed your spirit, he has given you hope where there was none.* It didn't matter whether Gary believed I could be restored. What mattered was that Stallings believed it.

This man was opening doors I had never known were there. I was fascinated by his imaginative search for the answers to my needs. Gary would have to deal with his problems in his own time and his own way.

CHAPTER 6

"Leola?"

I looked up. Gary was standing in the doorway of the bedroom. He looked gaunt and wan, deep purplish shadows spread beneath each eye.

"May I come in?" His voice was small, uncertain.

I nodded and gestured to the chair. He tentatively stepped through the door and smiled foolishly. My heart ached for him, he looked so defenseless and vulnerable.

"I thought we should talk, Leola. There's so much I want to say, to explain."

"S'okay," I rasped. My tongue and pharynx had healed enough to allow me to whisper.

"You sure?"

I nodded again and sat on the edge of the bed and waited as he fumbled for his cigarettes. His hands were trembling slightly. "Will it bother your throat if I smoke?" His voice cracked like an adolescent boy's.

"S'okay. Go ahead." Even if it did bother me I wouldn't have said so, he was in such obvious distress.

"I don't know what to say. I know I've been behaving badly. I"—his voice caught—"was wondering if we could try again?"

"Try what?" I whispered.

69

He shrugged. "You know."

"You want me to go to bed with you, is that it?"

"Yes," he whispered.

I didn't know what to say. He had hurt me deeply but now it was he who was stripped, defenseless, frightened.

"Please, Leo?"

I rose from the bed, and walked behind the chair and placed my hands on his shoulders, kneaded them gently. I didn't have to see his face to know he was crying.

"I feel like such a bastard, such a shit. I wake up screaming, Leo. I see your face," he slumped forward, his face buried in his hands. I stroked his head gently.

"I know," I whispered. "I know."

"I'm scared, I don't know what to do. How to act."

I continued to soothe with my whispers, tears stinging my eyes.

"I love you, Leo. You're the most beautiful thing that ever happened to me, me Tarzan. You were my dreams come true, I don't know if you can even understand that. I never had anything beautiful, not in my whole life and . . ."

He was crying too hard to speak; my throat was too constricted for me to even whisper.

He cleared his throat. "And when I saw you after the accident, I just couldn't take it. I couldn't take it, Leo. I know that's terrible, but your face, your beautiful face . . . Oh, God!"

I pressed my chest against his back and hugged him close, enfolding him in my arms.

"I want to try, Leo. Really I do."

I wept silently as I held him, unable to kiss him, to communicate the tenderness I felt. The tears ran down the face he couldn't take looking at. Tears that were somehow healing, that brought more relief than anguish.

"It's okay," I breathed into his ear.

"No. It's not okay. Can you ever forgive me?" He raised his head and looked up at me. Our eyes locked but I saw the flinch; it had been slight, but it had been there.

"What do you want?" I whispered. "What can I do?"

"Give me another chance. Could you, Leo? I wouldn't blame you if you didn't. I talked to Dr. Stallings again and he really does think he can fix everything."

"I know he does. But do *you* think he can?"

"I have to believe him. He wouldn't say it unless he could, would he?"

"I don't think so."

"So even if it isn't exactly like it was before, at least . . ." He looked down.

"At least I'll be presentable." I completed the sentence for him.

"I don't know if I can do it, Leo. Believe, I mean. But we should try, shouldn't we?'

"Yes, Gary."

He looked back up at me. This time he didn't flinch at all. "You mean it? You'll give me another chance?"

I nodded and would have smiled if I could have.

Daria was skeptical when I told her Gary and I were going to be all right. So was Dr. Stallings, although he didn't say so. I could feel it in his gaze as I explained that I had to give life with Gary one more try.

"I don't think we should postpone the surgery, Leo."

"What if I just stayed home for a couple of weeks." I whispered. "I know I'd feel easier in my mind instead of wondering and worrying."

"It's a lot to ask." He tapped a pencil on his desk. I didn't ask him to explain, I knew he meant I was asking for a miracle.

"I know it is. Really I do. But I can't not stay home for a while longer, it wouldn't be fair to Gary. This hasn't been easy for him."

"All right. Once again I have to tell you that you're leaving against my better judgment. But I do hope it works out."

"Thank you, Dr. Stallings. I knew you'd understand."

When I walked into the apartment I was as overwhelmed as I had been before—but in an entirely different way. The rooms were neat and clean. Gary had really knocked himself out. There was a bowl of flowers on the coffee table, so awkwardly arranged that the effect was wonderfully whimsical. Gary had bought groceries, even splurging on some really good soft cheeses.

"Do you think you can eat this?" he asked with a worried expression as he arranged the wedges on a large platter.

"If no one minds my using my fingers." I whispered. "I don't think I'm up to crackers yet."

"Oh, maybe I should have gotten something else."

"No, I can manage the brie. It looks just perfect."

"Would you like me to cut you some now?" He lifted the small wheel and put it on a plate.

"Shouldn't we wait for Daria and Bob?"

"They won't mind. I hope it's all right."

Gary cut the cheese; I poked my finger into it and scooped a dab into my mouth. Real food. My first taste since my peanut butter sandwich. It was the closest I had ever come to feeling pure ecstasy. "It's delicious," I whispered.

"No, I meant about asking Daria and Bob over. I hope it won't seem too much like last time."

"Let's forget about that, okay?"

He nodded eagerly.

"What can I do?" I whispered.

"Nothing, just sit and relax. I'm about to surprise you with a magnificent creation." I daubed another bit of cheese onto my finger and placed it on my tongue, convinced that it was the most delicious thing I had ever tasted. God, it was good to be home, to see Gary being so genuinely adorable. He must have spent hours cleaning, even the curtains had been washed and hung without a wrinkle.

I could feel a bubble of laughter trapped in my throat as I heard the sounds issuing from the kitchen. It seemed as if Gary was in there with a demolition crew; cupboards and drawers banging open and shut, metal clanking on metal. I decided to see if I could help, then thought better of it. This was *his* show, and by God he was courting me as he had never courted me before. There were even candles on the table, two places neatly set. He wanted dinner to be romantic. There would be time enough for us to share the chores later. I heard the whirr of the eggbeater. Could it be that he was attempting a soufflé? This I did have to see. I rose from the couch and walked quietly to the kitchen door for a peek.

Gary was slumped over the sink, the water running over his hands, his shoulders shaking. I backed slowly out of the door as he whispered, "Oh, God, oh God," over and over again. Numb with helplessness, I resumed my position on the couch and picked up the magazine.

"Leo?"

I looked up from the page. Gary was standing in the doorway, his face slightly red but otherwise composed.

"How about a drink?"

I nodded. He returned to the kitchen and emerged with a glass of red wine with a glass straw in it for me and a fresh beer for himself. My hands were trembling as I accepted the glass and carefully guided the straw between my teeth.

"Wait, Leo."

I looked across the coffee table to see Gary lifting the beer can.

"We should have a toast."

The straw swung recklessly around in the wine as I held my glass toward his.

"To us." I could see the pain in his eyes as our glasses touched. And for the first time since he had told me that he had asked Daria and Bob to join us, I was glad they were coming. I didn't like feeling so lost, so helpless. Their banter would help break the tension I could feel building between Gary and me.

At dinner Daria, sensing our discomfort, started a merry conversation about hospital shenanigans which led to a recap of Dr. Stallings' derring-do in the E.R. the afternoon I had arrived. Gary seemed genuinely interested, having never heard the details before.

"Then maybe he *can* do it," Gary said as he rose to carry the dishes back to the kitchen.

"Can do what, hon?" Daria asked.

"Give me back my Leo, the way she used to be."

There was an uncomfortable pause, I stared down at the table.

"If anyone can, *he* can," said Daria. "The man is a bloody genius."

"But has he done anything as . . ." Gary stopped.

"Hopeless?" I whispered.

"That isn't what I was going to say."

73

"None of that, Leo," said Daria. "You're not going to start the self-pity bit at this late date." She looked at me sternly. " 'Challenging.' Is that what you meant?"

"Yes."

Gary hurried to the kitchen with the dishes.

"Come on, Leo, don't be so ready for the worst. He's trying, look around you. And that soufflé he made, would you ever have imagined him doing anything like that? As hard as it is for you it's a big adjustment for him too."

"Bigger," I whispered.

"What do you mean?"

"He has to look at it all the time. I don't."

Daria opened her mouth to answer, then shut it and just gave me a hard look. I felt ashamed. She was right, I *was* letting self-pity get the upper hand.

"Okay, Leo, take it easy. All I'm saying is give the guy a chance. He really loves you."

"He loved the way I looked, he loved my face. What if I never get it back? What if Stallings can't do it?"

"He thinks he can. Don't you?"

"Yes. But no one knows for sure. What then?"

"Leo, Gary loves *you*, you're more than just a face."

"I wonder." My whisper was so quiet I'm surprised she heard it at all.

"Of course you are. Come on, chin up."

I glared at Daria and then made a sound closer to a giggle than any I had made since the accident. "If I *had* a chin, I wouldn't need you to tell me that."

Daria broke up.

"What's so funny?" Gary asked as he brought in a tray of coffee cups.

"Inside joke." I whispered.

We cleaned up the dishes together; Gary washed, I dried. He seemed to be taking an inordinate amount of time, rinsing each plate, spoon, glass, and pot with extreme care. I assumed he was stalling for time now that we were alone, really alone. No one was coming, no one to put off the moment when we would go to bed.

74

"It was a beautiful dinner," I whispered as I put the last pot away.

"Was it really? The soufflé fell."

"But it tasted wonderful, it really did."

"Leo?"

"Yes?"

"I really tried."

"I know you did."

"Do you? Do you really?"

I nodded and asked if he wanted a beer before bed.

"You wouldn't mind?"

"No. I'm tired. Not used to these late hours. You sit and relax, I'll get ready for bed."

I didn't hear him come into the bedroom; I was tired and had fallen asleep the moment my head touched the pillow. Early light was filtering through the curtains and I looked over at Gary's sleeping form, the sheets tangled around his legs, the blanket half on the floor. I shivered and straightened everything out, gently, trying not to disturb him. I studied the face; there were new lines etched around the eyes, even in repose. My poor darling Gary. I instinctively reached out and brushed his hair from his forehead. He stirred and sighed, then opened his eyes. The gaze was blank, unseeing, then slowly focused on me.

"Hi," he said. "I must have been dreaming."

I settled back on the pillows and stared up at the ceiling. It needed a coat of paint.

"Want to tell me about it?" My whisper was hoarse.

"I . . ." He rolled over, pulled the covers up around his hunched shoulders. "I dreamed it was all a bad dream."

God, how many times had I done the same thing?

"I dreamed we were the way we were. Dancing, having fun, laughing."

And what about the arguing? But that had been part of it too, the arguing had been part of the loving. It had enabled us to be free and open afterward, to make love with more passion. Would we ever do either one again?

I raised myself from the pillows on one elbow and began tracing the line of his neck with my fingers. Goose bumps rose instantly on

75

his flesh and he sighed. Maybe we could get through this after all. I continued to caress his neck, then the well-formed muscles in his arm. He reached for my hand with his and brought it around to his mouth and kissed my fingers gently. Would I ever feel the warmth of his surprisingly soft mouth on mine again? Would Stallings be able to make that sort of miracle possible? I began to tremble.

Gary slid from my embrace and put his feet on the floor. "I have to go to the bathroom," he muttered without looking at me. I lay back and watched him pad to the door, open it and then close it. Would anything ever be the way it was? I knew one thing: I'd never take anything for granted ever again. I heard a flush and then the sound of the shower. *It's okay. He's trying, he needs time.* I closed my eyes and drifted off to sleep. When I awakened again it was late morning, the bathroom door stood ajar. I sat up and listened, there wasn't a sound. Then I saw the note on the night stand. "Didn't want to wake you. Have gone to the market, be back soon." I slipped into a robe and walked to the kitchen for some juice.

Gary didn't return until late afternoon. I tried to fight off the fear and anger, the nagging conviction that he had stopped in a bar somewhere. When he finally showed up, he was laden with groceries and apologies. The distributor cap had blown off the car and he had had a devil of a time finding a parts place that was open. Right. It was Saturday. His hands bore grimy evidence that he was telling the absolute truth. I put the groceries away while he scrubbed his hands in the kitchen sink with Boraxo.

"How would you feel about going out tonight?"

"Out?"

"It was just a thought."

I tapped him on the shoulder and nodded. Dr. Stallings had said that I had to go forward, resume living, do what I would normally do. Within reason, of course. Our normal pattern had been to go to a bar, dance, and have a good time. He would understand if I disregarded his advice about staying away from restaurants and bars.

I dressed slowly, trying to put off the moment when the apartment door would shut behind us, remembering the last time I had gone out in public. Stallings talking: It really isn't necessary to put yourself through that kind of pain. Leola talking: Come on, it's not going to be that way forever, a night out never hurt anyone and at least the bars are dark. . . .

I dawdled over dressing and makeup until it was good and dark outside, then presented myself to Gary.

"All set?"

I wasn't, but I nodded anyway. We drove slowly into downtown Anchorage, Gary talking about his therapy, how well it was going. Obviously it was. It had already done wonders for him. A siren wailed in the distance and I cringed against the car door. Every detail of the accident, from the ambulance to the horrified stares in the Emergency Room, erupted in my mind. Was it always going to be like this? Would the sound of every siren I heard for the rest of my life trigger this response?

Gary gave me a quick look. "You okay, Leo?"

I stared out at the frozen expanse that stretched into the night. It must be like this on the dark side of the moon. What was I doing sitting in this car, going to a bar I didn't want to go to? The very thought of a drink made me feel slightly sick.

"You want to go home?" His voice was soft with disappointment.

I wanted to, more than anything. But where was home? I didn't know, not any more.

The bar was crowded but we were lucky and found a corner table. I leaned back into the shadows, steeling myself for the inevitable. It had happened the last time Gary and I had gone out and it happened again.

The cheery welcomes dissolved into unfinished statements. Horror, pity, hasty retreats beaten away from the table. It happened over, and over again, without fail, with every single man or woman who attempted to greet us. The odor of alcohol was oppressive, nauseating. If that guy hadn't been drunk at the wheel of his truck, I wouldn't be in this mess. My glass stood untouched on the tiny round table. *Take me home,* my mind screamed. No—take me back to the hospital. I can't go through with this charade. I can't act as if nothing is wrong. Again I wished fervently that Dr. Stallings hadn't been in the corridor, hadn't heard me strangling. Then I would have been spared all this.

Gary gestured toward my untouched drink. "Don't you feel well?"

I shook my head.

"Maybe if we danced for a bit? It might relax you."

I glared at him as though he had gone stark, staring mad.

He drew back as if he had been struck. "Bad idea. I'm sorry. It's just that you always loved to dance, I . . ." he struggled for control, tears were moistening his eyes, "I just thought it might take your mind off . . ."

I gripped the glass with such force it cracked and spilled its contents all over the Formica top of the table. Gary pulled a hankerchief from his pocket and mopped the puddle distractedly.

"You want me to take you home?"

I nodded. He reluctantly reached for the check, studied it and pulled some bills from his wallet. The night air stung my eyes and I stood in silence as Gary put the key into the car door. I felt a hundred years old.

"I'm sorry," I whispered.

"It's okay. Maybe it wasn't such a good idea to go out. What time do you have to be back at the hospital?" he asked as he switched on the ignition.

"In the morning." That wasn't true. Stallings had said I could check back in on Monday; tomorrow was Sunday.

I changed into my nightgown and slipped into bed. Gary was in the kitchen, rummaging in the refrigerator. I realized then that we hadn't eaten any dinner. It was all right, I wasn't hungry anyway. I heard the lights snap off in the living room then Gary's footfalls as he made his way across the dark bedroom. The bed sagged as he sat down, lifted the covers, and swung himself under the sheet. I lay motionless, feigning sleep. It would be better that way. He turned toward me and pulled my body against his. Dear God, I had dreamed of this, could it really be happening? Could this man who had been so proud of his beautiful wife really want me after all those stares in the bar?

I opened my eyes and touched his tense face hovering over mine. "I'm sorry, Leo. I just can't."

I reached up and wiped his wet cheeks with my hand.

In the hospital, Gary helped me unpack and lingered awkwardly near the bed.

"It's okay," I said, "You go on. I'll be all right."

"You will, Leo. I know you will. You're in good hands with Stallings. Everyone says he's the best. And I really believe that if anyone can make you the way you were, he can."

"And what if he can't?"

Gary looked away, unable to answer. I felt his grief; I knew he was mourning the wife who had died on impact on Tudor Road. And while I believed Dr. Stallings when he said he could restore me, I knew that the Leola Gary had married was gone for good. Gary hadn't bargained for that, and although he had tried valiantly to overcome his feelings, he had been humiliated beyond endurance, I could see that now.

"Gary," I whispered.

He looked at me expectantly, anxiety written all over his face.

"It's all right. Do what you have to do, I really do understand."

"You sure?"

I nodded and watched him leave the room, knowing it would be for the last time.

CHAPTER 7

In the morning I asked to be allowed to go back to full duty. Captain Laura said she wouldn't stand in my way if Stallings gave the go-ahead. I popped the question at the next available opportunity, cornering him in the corridor as he was making rounds.

He ran his hand distractedly through his sandy hair. "We'll discuss it later. See me in my office at 1500 hours." I nodded and made my way back to my room. My legs felt rubbery, and a knot of what I knew must be anger was constricting my chest. I walked uncertainly back to the desk where Susan was manning the phone.

"You have a visitor, Leola," she whispered, holding her hand over the receiver. I followed the direction of her gaze and saw Gary's social worker sitting on the couch in the waiting area. I walked over and stood in front of him and waited for him to tear his eyes away from the out-of-date *Newsweek*.

"Ah, Mrs. Cox." He didn't sound happy. "Is there somewhere we can speak privately?"

God, now what? Had something happened to Gary? I gestured for him to follow me and led him to the small room I now called home. I sat in the easy chair and let him take the hard-backed straight chair.

"I'll get right to the point."

That would be a nice change.

"Your husband has been making every effort to adjust to the situation. I'm sure you're aware of that?

I nodded.

"He's given his decision a great deal of thought, Mrs. Cox."

Get on with it!

"It's our considered opinion that his decision is for the best."

I reached for the slate that had been lying idle in the bed table drawer. I was not going to whisper to this creep. "GO ON;" I printed in block letters.

"Your husband feels it would be better in the long run if the marriage were dissolved now."

Dissolved? Marriages don't dissolve. "He wants a divorce?" I scribbled.

"In a word, yes. He wants you to have every chance for recovery. His enlistment is up and he will be returning to Florida to resume civilian life." He paused. "Mrs. Cox, this has been a very difficult decision for your husband. A marriage cannot survive that kind of distance."

"No." I printed.

"You won't give him the divorce?" There was alarm in the social worker's voice.

"No," I wrote. "A marriage can't survive distance."

He sighed with relief. "He wants you to have the apartment. That is, if you want it."

I nodded numbly, then leaned forward and whispered, "Why didn't he come himself?"

"Frankly, I advised against it. He's very distraught."

He's distraught! But I didn't, couldn't hate Gary. I still loved him in a hopeless way. He wanted out, I would have to accept that. Nor could I blame him, not really. I would probably always be a living reminder of his shattered hopes and dreams, of the beautiful wife he had so adored and who was forever gone. I couldn't hate Gary, but I hated this man facing me so coolly, this perpetual bearer of bad tidings. I picked up the slate and held it like a shield between us, then wrote: "All right."

As soon as he left the room I hurled the slate against the wall, against the calamity that had become my life. In an incredibly brief period of time I had lost my face, my baby, my husband. Above all, I had lost myself. Despite Dr. Stallings, I was not convinced that the

82

Leola who'd survived the accident that cost her lips, mouth, and chin was worth the effort of restoring them. I slumped back in the chair, closed my eyes, and prayed for oblivion.

I don't know how long I might have sat in that chair had Susan not appeared in the doorway.

"Leola, Major Stallings is waiting for you. In his office."

I hauled myself to my feet wearily and headed down the hall.

Dr. Stallings was at his desk, shuffling folders into a neat pile.

"Ah, there you are. I was beginning to worry."

"Worry?" I scribbled on the battered slate.

He looked at the message on the gray film. "Trouble speaking, Leo?" He rose and walked around the desk, placed his long, sensitive fingers on my neck, gently explored the glands there for swelling. "Open, wide as you can."

I opened my mouth, and jerked a little. It was still painful to open my jaw wide.

"Everything looks all right, what's the matter?" His deep baritone was kind, gentle.

I shook my head.

"Just don't feel like talking? That's not like you. Now," he sat on the corner of his desk, "tell me. How are your legs?"

I shrugged.

"Still weak?"

I nodded.

He reached over, picked up a file folder and flipped it open. "I don't think it would be advisable for you to go back to full duty just yet, you sustained quite a bit of trauma to the musculature. And since we're scheduling the next surgery relatively soon, it's vital that you have good blood vessel interaction. I know it's hard for you to have so much time on your hands with so little to do, but believe me, this pre-op period is crucial. In fact, you might be better off at home until we operate. How does that sound?"

I shrugged.

He leaned forward and looked right into my eyes. "What is it? Leo, don't withdraw now. Are you afraid I can't do it?"

I shook my head but stared down at my hands.

83

"Then, talk to me. Tell me what's wrong." His voice was soft but insistent.

"Nothing to go home to," I whispered.

Stallings sighed, closed the folder, and let it hang loosely across his knee. "I'm really sorry to hear that."

"Gary wants a divorce."

"Do you?"

"I don't know any more. It's an awful lot to ask of him."

"What is?"

"To wait, wonder."

Dr. Stallings moved to his feet and walked to the window behind his desk, then turned and leaned on the back of the swivel chair.

"The reconstruction will take time, of course. As for the wondering, I wish I could make him see what I see." His face brightened. "But I've studied everything carefully and I can promise you you won't have to hide your face in shame. Look . . ." he slipped into the chair and withdrew a series of beautifully executed sketches showing a step-by-step restoration of my face.

I felt a flutter of optimism in my heart. Thank God for this man. Thank God that he cared, that he wasn't treating me with clinical detachment. I felt myself swept along by his enthusiasm as he described how flesh and tissue could be remolded.

"I can really do it, I have to make you believe that."

"I believe you," I whispered.

"Good. I know I'm asking a lot, but whether you like it or not you have begun a remarkable journey. A journey forward away from fear and pain. I know it's hard to believe in view of everything that's happening right now but I want you to know, I'm in this with you. Who knows? We may even write some medical history while we're at it." His smile was contagious, and again I felt the tension begin to ease out of my body. "Meanwhile, I want you to get more photographs from home. Rest, don't knock yourself out. Can you do that?"

"I'll try." I got to my feet. Stallings walked around from behind the desk and took my hands in his. The flesh was warm, his touch delicate but firm. My hands tingled, it was as though hope were being transmitted from his hands into mine.

I walked slowly back to the little room, marveling at the effect Stallings always had on my spirits. *Watch it, Leola. He's a pro and so are you, let's not get emotional and silly just because he happens to be very good at his job.* I dialed Daria and asked if she could drop by before leaving for the day.

"What's up?" She asked as she charged into the room.

"Gary wants a divorce."

"You're kidding!"

"Afraid not."

"I'm really sorry, Leo. Not that it's happening, but that you must feel like you're being left in the lurch."

"In a way, but I do understand. He really tried, Daria."

"That's debatable."

"No, it's not. He tried the whole weekend—at everything. Believe me, he did. It will be better this way."

"That I won't argue with."

"He's going to move out of the apartment. Can you fix me up in officer's quarters until he's gone? I'm not up to full duty yet, and I see no point in hanging around here until I have to come back."

"Why go to the apartment at all? It's way off to hell and gone."

"I need to be by myself, and there's a lot of stuff I have to sort through."

"I don't know if it's such a hot idea for you to be alone right now."

"If it's not all right, believe me, you'll be the first to know."

"Promise?"

"Promise."

I spent the time "sorting through" the pitifully small store of effects Gary and I had accumulated during our brief time together. One by one I decided which items to keep, which to send to him, which to dispose of. I stifled my anger and fought the depression that resulted until I was exhausted. Daria came over several evenings and we played games. Chess. (I won.) Cribbage. (She won.) Double solitaire. Gin rummy. Shortly before ten o'clock she would go home, switching on the TV before she left. Often I awoke to find the screen humming, displaying a test pattern.

The days passed slowly; more photographs arrived from Ohio. I sent them to Dr. Stallings via Daria and ticked off another day on the calendar. Each day I grew a little stronger and found myself looking forward to the moment when we would begin "the journey." I began to discuss the surgery with Daria, how much I was looking forward to it.

"I have to agree with Stallings," Daria said as she stirred her coffee.

"What do you mean?"

"You're one hell of a woman."

"He said that?"

"That's what Susan told me. Said he's never met anyone like you."

I looked away from Daria, not wanting her to see the delight that must have been in my eyes. My heart was pounding at the thought of seeing him again. Come on, Leo. Pull yourself together, stop acting like a gaga schoolgirl.

"That's nice to hear," I whispered.

"Figured you'd like it. Come to think of it, I've never met anyone like you either. What time you want me to pick you up?"

"Whenever's convenient."

"I have to be in at eight. Seven o'clock all right?"

"I'll be ready."

My reappearance at the hospital for the pre-surgery check was an unexpectedly festive occasion. Daria had masterminded a party, complete with streamers.

Captain Laura had given orders that it must be held in the staff ladies' room—no other places were available—but that didn't seem to faze anyone, not even the male guests. Pastel balloons flew above the sinks and stalls. A sign—"Welcome back to the primordial ooze"— was posted above the door. It was, as nurse Susan remarked, the best ladies' room party in Alaskan history. Quite a few men attended, some of them looking wonderfully awkward and out of place. Dr. Gills was there, decked out in an extraordinary outfit that combined a plaid shirt, a tweed jacket and checked pants. He clasped my hand and led me in an old-fashioned Lambeth Walk, which was about all I was capable of. "Any time you're Lambeth way, any evening, any day." A strut. Daria had attended to the music and had somehow managed to borrow everything recorded that she knew I loved in the way of romantic ballads.

86

A squawk broke into "Some Enchanted Evening." Captain Laura, on the honker. She, too, was in a rare party mood. "Attention!"

We all condensed.

"Unauthorized, whatever-it-is down there, cut down on the noise. There's a panic up here—all the ambulatory patients are on their way downstairs!" An enthusiastic cheer echoed off the tile walls.

Dr. Stallings turned up at the very end of the party. He was dressed in the very cleanest of starched whites.

I could no longer keep up with the celebrants, and he knew it. He took one look at the staff—all properly off-duty—doing the twist, took my arm as if we were going to waltz, and led me out of the ladies' room.

"Let's go where we can talk," he said.

We walked to the elevator, rode up and strolled to his office. He settled in his chair and I took the one facing his desk, welcoming the opportunity to sink down and kick my shoes off.

"Seemed to be quite a party," he said.

I nodded, happy to be away from the din.

"Are you tired?"

"A little," I whispered.

He leaned forward to hear me better; I drew my chair closer to the desk.

"Leo, things aren't progressing as quickly as I had hoped."

My heart sank. "Why? What's wrong?"

"Nothing is wrong. Not really. A jaw operation is necessary before I can . . ." He paused. "We have to get the jaw reconstruction out of the way, bridges for the teeth, replacements of other missing parts. . . ."

"Doctor, please. You forget I'm a nurse. Tell it to me straight. What's the hang-up?"

He pulled my file from the pile and opened it.

"Where are we now?" I asked. "What has to be done first?"

"Well, it won't be the jaw bone, as I had hoped."

"Why not?"

"Oh, I'll operate on the sixteenth as scheduled. But so much needs to be done on the jaw bone, we'll have to postpone that until April."

"Why?"

"I have to have teeth to put in the jaw; they won't be ready soon enough. Some people take longer to do their jobs than others." He didn't say any more. I understood.

˙ "So here's what I propose. I'll do an outer-mouth plasty on you first, on the sixteenth."

"Okay."

"Well, maybe not. I have to tell you that it will make you look worse than you do now."

I found that hard to conceive and just stared at him, waiting for the rest.

"You'll have temporary teeth—not the permanent crowns and bridges. You'll have a fleur-de-lis twist of the skin surface, borrowing a patch from the upper lip to the lower. Instead of three-quarters of your mouth bashed, the way it is now, you'll have the whole thing bashed."

"At least that will make everything consistent."

"Your whole mouth, except for a tiny slot for a straw, will be sewn together. You'll be able to drink, but not to chew. And you won't be able even to whisper."

"For how long?"

"At least six weeks."

I was trying to envision my mouth looking any worse than it did now.

He reached across the desk and gently touched my arm. "I know it's asking a lot after all the pep talks I've been giving you. But I can't do the surgery without your knowing you're going to come out of it looking worse than when you went in."

"You mean it has to get worse before it gets better?"

"In a sense. But I want to be sure you trust the plan I have for you."

As if I had any choice!

"Not only my plan," he continued. "You have to trust my hands, my mind, my whole heart. I had hoped the first surgery would produce a more dramatic improvement. That you would be able to see your jaw outlined again. Somehow, I know, bone is easier to believe in."

"Tell me more about the fleur-de-lis."

"That's plastic surgery to remove scar tissue. It's a skin patch from there to here. Always vertical, and in your case it will be from up to down." His hands plied the air gracefully. "A patch is thinly sliced off, so thin we know that what is left will grow again—it will be separated from the skin surface by all but a very thin slip at the bottom. This is twisted around and the life-giving side is placed down and onto the injured area. New life will grow in both parts. There will be a tiny scar from the twist, but that can be corrected later."

"How long before I get back to where I am now?"

"I know this sounds like a setback, Leo. But actually it isn't. Not when you realize that from that point on we'll really be able to go forward."

"What choice do I have?" I whispered. "I've already fallen off the cliff. Now you're asking me to jump again."

"Yes, but with one difference."

"What's that?"

"I'll be there to catch you this time."

From the hours I had already spent reading up on the subject of plastic surgery, I knew the fleur-de-lis operation had been developed by more than one plastic surgeon—three guys named Stein, Abbe, and Eastland. The procedure, still fairly new, was dubbed fleur-de-lis because when it was finished that portion of the patient always looked like an overblown iris—the flowering spring bulb we always called a "flag" back in Ohio—the symbol of royal France.

Fortunately or unfortunately, I understood exactly what Dr. Stallings was planning. Once when I was a very small child I had been taken to an amusement park and found myself—by accident, I suspect—seated at the top of a very long, convoluted, twisting slide. "Here you go!" said some stranger. I felt a whack on my rump and down I flew.

That's how I felt now, facing Dr. Stallings. A frightened child at the top of an enormous slide. He took my hand in his.

"I know how much you've been through already. I know the way people have looked at you, including some of those you care most about. I know how hard it is to take."

Something about his voice told me that he *did* know. I looked at him numbly.

"But inside, you're still the person you always were."

89

I shook my head slowly. "No, that's the first thing you've said that isn't true. I was who I was at least partly because of my looks. I don't know who I am any more. Why do you think Gary left me? He left because that woman no longer exists."

"He couldn't see what I see."

"Of course not," I whispered. "He isn't a surgeon. He's just a nice, decent guy who fell in love with a face."

"I see more than a face. Now it's going to be your turn to start recognizing what I already have."

"What's that?" It wasn't so much a whisper as a hiss.

"That you're a woman of remarkable courage. You have humor, intelligence, resolution. And heart. You haven't suddenly developed those qualities over the last few months, Leo. They were always there, you just never had to depend on them before. Here's your chance to discover what I see and feel is there."

You wouldn't say those things if you really knew me. I'm stubborn, willful, vain. As for those things you say I am, I don't think I'm any of them. My thoughts sounded so loud within my head I thought he must be able to hear them.

Distant laughter filtered up from the parking lot below the window. My party was over; people were moving out to their cars. People with mouths, lips, chins. People who had the capacity to laugh and love.

"All right, Doctor. I'll do it. Let's see if we can make some history."

"Never mind the history, Leo. We're going to fix everything."

"Good as new?"

"Better. Better than anything you can imagine."

"Have you been drinking?"

He looked startled for a moment, then smiled. "No, I'm high on my vision of what we're going to do together. Wait and see."

That I could do. What other choice did I have?

CHAPTER 8

On the sixteenth, I checked back into the hospital and was processed like any other patient. It made me feel awkward and ill at ease. This was my hospital, I knew its procedures better than most; yet here I was filling out the endless forms while the staff kept perfectly straight faces. Finally, I was motioned on to Receiving.

An orderly arrived with a wheelchair. I stayed on my feet, whispering that I really didn't need it.

"Sorry," he whispered back, "regulations."

I sighed and sank obediently into the chair.

It was late afternoon; by this time tomorrow I would look worse than ever. I was beginning to have second thoughts, all right. The orderly wheeled me off and I spent the balance of the day going through the conventional pre-op tests.

Daria popped by for a visit before going home for the evening. "Well, are you all set?"

"As set as I'll ever be. Now don't forget. Stallings says I'm going to look worse than ever."

"I know. Try and remember he also says that's only going to be temporary."

"Let's hope."

"It will. Stallings isn't one to mince words, you ought to know that by now."

"I do. It's just hard to imagine looking worse. This has been bad enough."

"I know it has, Leo. But at least this is a beginning, you're on your way, kid."

"I hope so."

"Of course you are. You think you'll be able to sleep? Do you want me to have them bring you something?"

"I'll be okay, don't worry."

"I won't. See you tomorrow." She gave me a quick kiss and left.

I lay back on the bed and closed my eyes. Tomorrow a new dawn. Surgeons always operate at sunrise. I wondered why and made a mental note to ask Dr. Stallings.

Actually they didn't come for me at dawn. The surgery was started at eight minutes past eight. The two nurses who came to prep me were two women in their mid-thirties whom I knew only slightly. That was standard hospital procedure, as I well knew. A staff member admitted for surgery—even if only for removal of a nasal passage wart—is purposely isolated from his or her friends. Emotions or wisecracks might break the concentration, distract the staff from their duties.

One nurse taped my wedding band without a word or glance. It was written on the orders: "Tape wedding ring." I had come in without any other jewelry, I couldn't imagine why I hadn't thought to leave the ring behind.

I insisted on a local anesthetic.

"Want to keep tabs on me, Leo?" Dr. Stallings asked through his mask.

"No, I want to help. Won't the blood circulate better if I'm not all the way under?"

"It sure will." I could see the concern in his eyes. And the admiration.

"Good. Let's get started then."

Dr. Stallings worked rapidly. He was assisted by Dr. Sessions, who I knew was a good tennis player; Nurse Sgt. Francis handled the instruments. They all did the job in one hour and twenty-eight minutes.

92

The jaw wire was removed and my lips were sewn together, just as Stallings had described. As I was wheeled out of the operating room, I passed under a sign: *Onward and Upward.* In the elevator, someone had taped up another one: *Give 'Em Hell Next Week.*

I had the feeling I wouldn't want to wait that long.

Later in the afternoon Dr. Stallings dropped by. The smile on his face made me feel almost giddy.

He made a little bow. "The patient tolerated the procedure and left the operating room in good condition. It really went well." Another, even wider smile, then he reached into his pocket and withdrew a new slate. "For a fresh start." He handed it to me.

I wrote my first message: "I want to see."

"Sure you feel up to it?"

I nodded.

"Well, as it so happens, I came prepared." He reached into his white coat pocket; this time he pulled out an old-fashioned hand mirror, a smaller edition of the kind with a handle that women used to keep on their vanity tables. "Now remember, it's pretty bad. Probably worse than whatever you've been imagining."

I gave a small nod to indicate that I was prepared.

"Now?"

I held out my hand for the mirror. He handed it to me, the gesture dragged into slow motion by his obvious apprehension. As for me—no matter what greeted me in the mirror, no matter how grotesque I might look—I was determined not to let it throw me. I wanted this man who had literally put himself on the line for me to know I really was willing to go to any length to cooperate.

He carefully removed the dressing and I steeled myself. It *was* bad, no doubt about it. My stomach lurched at the sight of my lower lip, of the skin being repaired by borrowing from one of the few undamaged areas on my chin.

"Just a short-term merger," Dr. Stallings said. His eyes had followed mine as I studied the reflection.

A V-shape of flesh was flipped up and spread to make a Y, covering a horizontal slash.

"The idea," he continued, "is to fix up a contracture. I had to pull together the anguished skin which had shrunk and was clinging to

93

the nearest whole surface. As you can see, it worked. The contracted surface is now covered with a light blanket of whole skin."

I set the mirror down on the bed and reached for the slate. "You weren't kidding," I wrote, my hand trembling.

"About looking bad?"

I nodded.

"I'll never lie to you, Leo. We've both got some long, rough times ahead and if I say you're going to look bad for a while, then you're going to look bad."

"And if you say I'll look good?" I scribbled.

"You'll look good. That's a promise."

"Terrific!"

He read the slate and grinned. "I think so too. It's going to get more and more exciting as we go along."

Maybe he was crazy. Maybe I was, too. But I returned the small salute he tossed my way before heading out the door.

Daria, for once, was speechless. She stood in the doorway, frozen in her tracks. "Jesus, Leo!" she said finally. "I had no *idea*!"

I beckoned for her to come in and pointed to the chair, then picked up the slate: "He *said* it would be worse before it got better."

"Well, he wasn't kidding." She hoisted up her tote bag and pulled out a large volume. "Bob thought you might want to improve your mind while you were hanging around with nothing to do. Actually it has some pretty pictures." She placed the book on my lap; it was a beautifully illustrated collection of archeological discoveries in Greece.

I clasped it and squeezed my eyes in thanks.

"Don't mention it," she quipped.

After she had gone, I leafed through the pages of the book, stopping to study the chapter on the discovery of the Winged Victory of Samothrace, or the Nike as the sculpture is now called. She is the first thing you see upon entering the Louvre in Paris, I read, and museum-goers taking their first look at her go away feeling that they have had a stunning experience.

Not unlike the way people react when they *see me*, I thought. Only there is stunning and there is *stunning*.

I read on. The Winged Victory was dug up on an island in the Aegean Sea. She's 2,000 or so years old. Her garments flow over the lower body, leaving exposed the beautiful breasts, and magnificent wings that seem to be just coming to rest after a long flight. But one foot is broken, there's almost nothing of her arms—arms that should have been flung upward in ecstasy—and no head at all. No head.

When they first dug her up, archeologists assumed that the Nike's head and arms were missing. Closer examination revealed that the sculptor had made her with arms that stopped just beyond the shoulder and had never given her a head at all.

In the morning, when Dr. Stallings dropped in, I showed him the Nike. "Is that the price of victory?" I wrote on the slate.

Dr. Stallings smiled. "No, not in these days."

"That's good. I don't have wings either."

"You have a spirit that will allow you to soar, Leo."

I looked at him long and hard. He certainly was the most unusual doctor I had ever met. In fact, he was the most unusual man I had ever met.

In time, I was summoned for a post-operative checkup. At such a session they don't tell you anything on the spot, of course. They just take the dressings off and say things like, "Hmmm," and "Once more, please," and "That's it, thank you." There must be no inflection in anyone's voice that might give the patient a hint of what's what—the noncommittal tone is drilled into nurses.

I peeked to see what Dr. Stallings was writing. He didn't write much, maybe two lines. Good. When they write a lot, that's bad. I craned my neck and read: *February 27, 1969. V-Y Sulcoplasty. Clean. Patient appears good condition.*

No accounting for taste, I thought. Everything near my mouth—on both sides, above, and below—was red and swollen. And my chin, neck, and the area beneath my ears were twenty-five percent worse than before the surgery.

As for my jaw, it still made me think of a broken railroad track with major bridges washed out. But maybe that could be fixed. Stallings seemed to think it could. I wondered how he'd do it: fill it with steel or plastic? As for the outside skin, if the V-Y took—and apparently it was doing just that, and several other procedures too—in the distant future I just might get back enough of a face to avoid people's staring.

I returned to my room and spent some more time studying the ravages of surgery in the hand mirror. I had begun to achieve a kind of clinical detachment in an attempt to see my face as Dr. Stallings saw it. It was then that I noticed something I had overlooked until now. On one-quarter of my mouth, there was no lip. How could I have not noticed? I was dumbfounded. A fourth of the reddish part, the place where you put the lipstick, the kissing part, was gone! Then I remembered: The report Stallings had shown me that detailed the emergency surgery of last November . . . *Upper right. Tissue excised and discarded.*

I knew that plastic surgery could work wonders with similar skin borrowed from all over the body. The seams would show but at least there would be a continuous surface. But the fact was, the reddish mucosa of my mouth on the upper right side was *gone*. It was gone as surely as though I had lost a finger or a foot. And for that, I knew from my reading, there were no spare parts handy. Just how would I explain this particular deformity? Bitten off by a lover who got carried away?

Dr. Stallings had said I could go home until our next appointment. I slammed my possessions into a suitcase and checked myself out of the hospital. On the way home in the car, I diagnosed my symptoms: I was sinking into a subclinical depression. Instead of driving to Daria and Bob's and asking them for help, I headed straight for the apartment. To hell with it, to hell with everything!

Daria called several times a day and I tapped out the code for yes, I'm okay. When she offered to come over, I tapped a loud No! I brushed off two other well-meaning friends who came by with groceries. When I was alone I sat before the TV with the lights off staring blankly at the fuzzy images. The antenna was broken. I could have gotten a message to Bugler easily enough but I didn't bother. The apartment was a mess. I left it that way.

Daria finally came over—uninvited—and urged me to move back

to the Base. I refused. I sent her away with a message for my superiors at the hospital, asking if I might go back to work. They refused.

Daria came back. "Leo, Captain Laura feels you can't hack the job right now."

I looked away like a petulant four-year-old.

"Come on, stop acting this way. Even if they just put you to work counting Band Aids, it will wear you down. You don't want to slow down your recovery, do you?"

I still wouldn't look at her.

"Let me put it to you this way: if you're inattentive because you're worn out and someone croaks, how will you feel?"

Now I looked at her—a nasty scowl.

I was convinced that there was no real question of my own health or competence. The truth was I looked so horrible they didn't want me walking the halls frightening the patients. I snatched the slate and wrote, "You mean *scare* someone to death?"

"Come on, Leo. This isn't like you. You knew you were going to look worse after the surgery. I don't blame them for not letting you work yet; you need to build up your strength, and you probably *would* scare some poor patient. Is that so terrible? Or is that what you want? People reacting to poor Leola's ravaged face?" She was on the verge of tears.

I stared at her, stupefied. My hands were shaking as I wrote very precisely that I had just discovered my lip was beyond repair. I handed her the slate.

Daria sat for a moment studying the carefully printed lines. Then she looked up and cleared her throat. "Does Stallings say it's irreparable?"

"Sez nothing. Report sez lip was discarded!!!!!"

"Well, of course I haven't read the report. But I'd think Stallings would have told you if nothing could be done."

"Need comparable tissue," I printed.

"I understand that. Why don't you speak to him about this? I can't believe he'd build you up the way he has if your lip can't be repaired. He probably has a solution."

"Needs a miracle."

"Maybe. I've heard he's worked a few."

"Really!!!"

"Yes, really! In fact, you know he has. So why don't you stop this nonsense and go see him."

"Okay!"

"Stop pounding that slate so hard, you'll wear it out. Why don't you write everything down, all your questions, and take them in. Unless . . ." she paused.

I looked at her expectantly.

"You enjoy being this way."

"You win," I wrote slowly.

"It's not a matter of winning, Leo. I know you better. I also think you've been driving yourself crazy with worrying and too much knowledge. You've really got to start being a better patient and trusting your doctor."

"I trust him."

"Most of the time I think you do. But do me a favor and stop second-guessing, will you? At least not until you've gone over this with Stallings."

"Okay."

She rose and put on her coat. I walked her to the door.

"It's okay, it really is. Feel better, will you?"

I nodded.

After she left, I realized I already *did* feel better. Daria was right; I had been really doing a job on myself. I prepared for bed, resolved to go to Elmendorf first thing in the morning. I picked up a note pad, climbed under the covers and began to write my questions for Dr. Stallings in a neat, clear hand.

Even though it was bad form, I barged into his office with the pad in hand. He looked up in surprise. "Trouble?"

I nodded and sat down in the chair. I handed him the pad and watched him as he read my questions.

"To begin with, I personally think I *can* restore the lip. I'm working on an idea now, and when the time comes you'll be fully informed."

"Any chance it won't work?" I wrote.

"Yes, but I'm more interested in the chance that it will. I've also certified you to return to limited work."

I felt like jumping up and hugging him.

"I'll arrange for you to be in Surgical Recovery, where I can keep an eye on you. A desk job for starters."

"Beats TV," I wrote.

"Yes, I expect that could drive anyone crazy."

"Thanks!" I scribbled.

"Don't mention it."

"Ha ha, very funny," I wrote.

"You know what I mean. Report for duty in the morning and Leo, please try and get some rest."

I stood and saluted him smartly.

CHAPTER 9

It didn't take me long to realize the reasoning behind my assignment to Surgical Recovery. I was relatively isolated there, and the patients were in no condition to react to my appearance. Most of them wouldn't have noticed if Dracula was hovering over them.

As Daria had predicted, much of the work involved inventorying medical dressings and supplies. Even so, I was grateful for the job. It gave me a sense of some purpose, got me out of the apartment, and gave me ample opportunity to see Dr. Stallings.

From time to time he would pop into my tiny office. He always seemed cheerful, resolute, hopeful—and he never mentioned a thing about my lip. Had he solved the problem? Presumably not, since I knew he'd rush to tell me. Then what was he always so damned cheerful about? Under any other circumstances I would have suspected him of being smitten. He was manifesting symptoms I had observed in men for several years and, in all honesty, had enjoyed. But to think this could be the case now was too bizarre for words. Whenever I saw him approaching I straightened my slumped back, raised my head and looked at him expectantly. I was determined not to push him for an answer; he would talk to me about my lip when he was good and ready. However spontaneously he might act in a crisis, I now knew that he was an extraordinarily meticulous surgeon.

If he didn't have time to stop in the office, he would rap a smart rat-a-tat on the door frame. That offhand manner didn't fool me. He was checking me out.

I could understand my own excitement at seeing him; my life was literally in his hands. But he seemed to be experiencing something too, something I couldn't quite put my finger on. No matter how hard I tried to dismiss it, the feeling persisted. I contemplated requesting some time with a psychiatrist and dismissed that. Surely he would think me completely mad were I to present him with a carefully written statement that I felt that the most brilliant plastic surgeon on the staff had eyes for me. They'd lock me up and throw the key away. Write me off as having delusions, possibly something worse.

No, it had to be something else. Clinical interest? Yes. But I really could sense something more than clinical interest and it alarmed me. I feared for my own sanity.

"How goes it?" Daria asked.

"Okay," I wrote.

"You mean better than doing nothing."

I nodded.

"Any news on your lip?"

"Not yet."

"Hang in there. You know he's working on it."

I nodded. She was beginning to look quite pregnant. I slumped over my inventory sheets at the thought; there but for that truck driver would have gone I . . . I rubbed my eyes with my knuckles. Then, feeling a presence in the room, I drew my hands away and looked up.

"You look like Anchorage harbor at low tide." Dr. Stallings had entered the room so quietly that I hadn't heard him. "Are you all right?"

I nodded and straightened my back.

"Well, I dropped by to tell you you're going to have some company. Remember Michael from the children's ward?"

Michael! The child I had held up as a paragon to Gary. My God, that seemed centuries ago. I nodded and wrote, "Yes, I remember

102

Michael. I taught him to read." First I had read to him and then I taught him the old-fashioned way: A is for apple, American, aircraft.

"You must have done a good job," said Stallings. "He just heard that you had been in an accident, now he says he's going to come and read to *you*."

No, no! I shook my head, gestured at my face. "Keep him out of here." I wrote.

Dr. Stallings grinned. "I'm afraid that's easier said than done. They've given him an electric-powered wheelchair. He's whizzing around the hospital like it's Monaco at Grand Prix time. There's talk of sandbagging the corners."

When he leaned forward across my desk, I had no choice but to meet his gaze, and I didn't want to do that because I was getting that feeling again—a current of something—and it was beginning to distress me.

"Leo, I've seen many gravely injured people in my relatively short time in medicine. The ones who get through best are those who surrender their pride and accept help and love when it's offered to them. I know you know that as well as I do. But you've got to stop this intellectualizing and realize that you are not some kind of exception. Tell me, where is it written that you must suffer alone?"

I averted my gaze and fumbled for my slate in the pile of inventory sheets littering my desk.

"Michael has been told that you don't look the same."

"Fine," I wrote. "But how much does he understand?"

"I don't know, but I wouldn't underestimate him. He understands he wants to see you. Don't you think the moment may have come for you to start taking some emotional risks? I know, it's been a brutal experience and you have good reason to want to withdraw from the outside world.

"I know you must feel enormous grief over your husband's inability to nurture you through this. But, Leo, chances are the marriage would have failed anyway. What you have to ask yourself is whether that's true."

Everything he was saying was absolutely true and I was furious. Why did I have to take all the risks? It wasn't fair.

He leaned back, studying my eyes. "I guess I'm being presumptuous."

"You are," I said, the slate held in front of me with both hands.

He flinched. Funny, he never flinched when he looked at me. "I'm sorry."

"Don't be. You're right." I wrote shakily.

"I am?" He seemed really relieved.

"Probably wouldn't have worked."

"How about Michael?"

"Not ready."

"I disagree."

I knew it was pointless to argue. I was going to see Michael whether I wanted to or not. "When?" I wrote.

"When he gets here. Why do you think your marriage would have failed? Don't answer if you feel I'm prying."

"It's okay. Was mostly physical."

"The attraction?"

I nodded.

"Well," he said, "that's nothing to flog yourself about. Many young people make that mistake, it's not a unique situation."

I nodded, knowing he was right. But there was also something else, a tone of enormous sadness in his voice. I wondered if he felt he had made the same mistake? After all, hadn't he married a fellow student while still in school? Maybe the two of them were becoming polarized. I knew now that Gary and I had been, long before the accident. It wasn't just the loss of my face that had driven Gary away.

"Sometimes," Stallings was saying, "we naively think that we can remold the other person, change them. We call it 'helping' them, of course."

I flinched at this direct hit. Almost from the beginning I had tried to mold Gary into what I thought he should be, pushing him to go to school, to grow up, to "better" himself.

"Of course," Dr. Stallings mused, "the effect is the reverse of what we intend."

Again I wondered if he was thinking of his own marriage—then dismissed the thought. Don't assume anything, Leo. That's what you did with Gary; you assumed he wanted the same things you did. What had Gary wanted? Suddenly, for the first time, I faced the

104

painful truth: Other than a beautiful wife and a good time, I had no idea.

"The rift becomes wider, the gap gets harder to bridge," Stallings was saying. "We begin to resent the other person for not living up to whatever preconceived image we've fixed in our minds."

I couldn't imagine Dr. Stallings resenting anyone. Was it possible that his wife resented him? A vague image of a concert poster floated into my mind. The one I had seen going up on the Municipal Auditorium that morning when Tudor Road still lay ahead of me.

"Acceptance is the key to everything, Leo. I don't mean that we have to accept the worst that life deals us. But we do have to learn how to recognize our own limitations. The irony is, once we accept our limitations, there then is no limit to what we can do. For example, your case. I have to accept what there is to work with. I know you've been worrying about the mucosa problem. I have too, but I have not accepted the fact that it can't be repaired. If that were so, I would have told you right away."

"What are you going to do?" I wrote.

"I haven't quite solved it yet, but I'm going to. In the meantime, you have to accept the fact that this is a difficult period *and* that there are people who care about you. You have more friends here than you realize. People you've given unstintingly to. Is it just a one-way street with you? Do you always have to be the one who gives?"

"No," I wrote.

"Then accept whatever comes, especially the caring. There's no reason for you to suffer so much isolation."

"Can't go out, you know that."

"I'm not talking about that and you know it. I'm talking about emotional isolation. I think the time has come for you to discover the real depth of your resources."

"What if I don't have any?"

"Leo, I would be willing to bet my whole career as a surgeon that you have resources far beyond anything you've ever imagined."

I stared down at the heap of papers, feeling defenseless and awkward.

"Here," Dr. Stallings dug into his pocket. "I brought you these. Try them on for size."

He was holding a gray plush jewel box. I stared at it, bewildered.

105

He placed it gently in my right hand, and I opened the catch. Earrings nestled on the satin. Jade. The semiprecious stone everyone brings home from Alaska. These were simple ovals, with thin gold-filled frames and stud fasteners.

"As your surgeon," he said with a grin, "I noted that the patient has pierced ears. If your lobes are clogged I'll be glad to drill them again."

I fingered the earrings, the jade was warm and smooth to the touch.

"Go ahead," he urged, "try them on. This is a real occasion. Michael may show up at any moment."

I looked at Dr. Stallings in wonderment. What a thing to do! I carefully removed the backing from one of the earrings and tried to insert the post in my earlobe.

"Here," he said, "allow me."

I felt like a little girl as he gently placed the earring in my ear. What a thoughtful man he was. Not at all like some of the surgeons who strutted through Elmendorf, advertising their importance. Marching as though they thought they were God's gift to humanity. He placed the second earring and I adjusted the backings, let my hands drop and looked at him expectantly.

"Very becoming," he said.

"Thank you *very* much," I wrote.

"You really like them?"

I nodded. "Always wanted jade earrings."

He beamed with pleasure. "I was afraid you might already have some."

We both turned toward the door as the sound of quick running footsteps echoed out in the hall. Then a cry—"Michael, slow down! Turn right. Put it in low gear!"—then a gentle bump at the door. Dr. Stallings opened it and Michael wheeled himself in, accompanied by a nurse. The powered chair halted in front of my desk and there was my star pupil, dressed in a red tartan bathrobe. His gray eyes twinkled with mischief; his nurse was clearly out of breath. Under one arm he clutched a thin children's book. I snatched up a file of papers and held it in front of my lower face.

"Hey, Nurse Leo, I'm sure glad to see you."

I kept the folder in front of my face for a moment, feeling a bit like Mme. DuBarry with her fan. Then I slowly lowered my hands so that Michael could have a full view of the damage. This was what Dr. Stallings had planned, had wanted. Okay, let him see what happens. Maybe then he'll stop looking at me through rose-tinted glasses.

Michael's face was still shining. "Gee, I've missed you. We all missed you. Where have you been? Oh, that's right, you've been hurt. Hey, watch this." He executed a few figure eights with his wheelchair. "Great, huh?"

I nodded.

"Take it easy, Michael," Dr. Stallings said quietly. "You know that Nurse Leo can't talk?"

The boy nodded. "Yep, I know. That's why I brought this along." He held up the book, *The Velveteen Rabbit.* "You'll be real proud of how I can read. I'm even reading all the little kids to sleep."

He turned his chair expertly, brought it to snug harbor at the side of the desk, looked directly at my face with a confident smile and said, "You'll like this one. Or have you read it already?"

I shook my head slowly.

Michael turned to Dr. Stallings. "You can listen, too, if you want," he said magnanimously.

Dr. Stallings hitched himself up on the corner of the desk; Michael ceremoniously opened the book and began to read.

"There once was a Velveteen Rabbit . . . and in the beginning he was really splendid!" He looked up, flashed a smile and read a few lines in his thin, musical voice. Then he set the book down on his lap. "You see, Nurse Leo, he was a Christmas toy and he got played with and played with and got all worn out. Then the children that owned him grew up and went away to school. The rabbit was put away in a toy closet with a whole bunch of other toys . . ." Michael glanced sternly at Dr. Stallings, who had snuck a glance at his watch. "Are you listening?"

"Oh, yes. What happened next?"

"Well, you see the children got told by their parents and teachers about real rabbits and real dogs and real horses. So they forgot about the toys. But there was a model horse called Skin Horse, he was the head of all the toys in the closet . . ."

I caught Dr. Stallings' eye and he smiled. We were both amused at the way Michael was obviously embellishing the original story.

"And the children said, 'Well this isn't a real horse'—trying to put Skin Horse down, you know . . .''

Dr. Stallings leaned forward toward Michael and said softly, "Michael, why don't you just read us the words in the book. We don't know the story and we'd really like to hear it."

"Right!" Michael said with a twitch. He waited a moment for the spasm to pass and then resumed reading. "The Velveteen Rabbit asked the Skin Horse. 'What does it mean to be real? Does it mean to have things buzz inside you?'" He looked earnestly at me, "You know, Nurse Leo, like those stupid buzzing toys that never work."

I nodded.

"And the Skin Horse said, 'Real isn't how you are made. It's a thing that happens to you. When a child loves you for a long long time, not just to play with but really loves you . . . then you become real.'

" 'Does it hurt to become real?' asked the Velveteen Rabbit. 'Sometimes,' said the Skin Horse. 'By the time you are real most of your skin has been rubbed off . . .' "

"*Loved* off!" corrected the nurse.

" 'Loved off,' " Michael continued. " 'By the time you are real your hair has been loved off and your eyes dropped out and you get loose in the joints and very shabby. But these things don't matter at all. . .' "

The book suddenly slid off his lap and tumbled to the floor. Michael drew a four-ply surgical tong from his pocket, picked it up, and resumed reading. " 'But these things don't matter at all . . . because once you are real . . . you can't be ugly . . . except to people who don't understand.' "

For some moments none of us said a word. Dr. Stallings and I rose and, as if on unspoken cue, we all three joined hands in an awkward, lopsided circle. We stood that way for a moment, then Michael slipped his hand out of mine, switched on his wheelchair and made for the door. His nurse barely got there ahead of him to open it.

"He's in really fine fettle today," she said as the wheelchair hummed off into the hall.

I bowed my head: My tears were falling all over the little jewel box that had held the inexpensive jade earrings. *Jade is green. Green means go. Go ahead. Be real.*

I looked up to find myself alone in the room. Dr. Stallings had slipped away without a sound.

CHAPTER 10

"Well," Daria said as she sank into the chair facing my desk, "I don't know about you, but I'm beat." She pushed the chocolate malt she had brought up from the cafeteria across the desk and fished a straw out of the bag. "You did want chocolate, didn't you?"

I nodded and pulled the wrapper off the straw while she unwrapped her sandwich and pried the lid off her container of coffee.

"Not exactly the Ritz, but it beats the noise in the cafeteria."

I sipped the shake and nodded.

"You know, Leo, I've been thinking a lot about you and Stallings."

Something about her tone made me decide not to look up; she was too good at reading my eyes. I waited for her to go on.

"I may be crazy, but I think he feels more than a doctor-patient kindredship."

I grabbed the slate. "You *are* crazy!"

"Don't get excited. I'm not implying there's any hanky-panky going on. That's not his style, or yours for that matter. It's just something I feel. A sort of special tension, if you know what I mean."

I scribbled, "You're imagining things." What would she say if she knew I had been feeling the same thing? I wasn't about to agree with her. If anything, her confirmation had frightened me badly.

"No, I don't think so. He's dedicated, that's true. He has terrific

111

compassion for all his patients, that's true. But Leo, when he talks about you, his face positively *shines*."

I took a deep swig on the straw and almost choked.

"When he talks about you it's not just like he's discussing an interesting case. It's almost as if you keep him off balance somehow. Like you were some sort of force of nature that he's trying to keep in check."

"Phooey!" I wrote.

"It's true. You wait, you'll see."

"Too many novels."

"Maybe. But I really don't think so. I am getting some interesting vibes. Even though he's married, more's the pity."

"I KNOW HE'S MARRIED." I printed the letters; my equivalent of raising my voice.

"Wonder what she's like?" Daria persisted. "Have you ever met her?"

I shook my head.

Daria took a bite out of her sandwich and chewed thoughtfully. "Neither have I. Doesn't that strike you as odd?"

"No. Don't travel in social circles."

Daria consulted her watch, finished her sandwich, and stuffed the wrapper in the bag. "Well, when you get over being mad at me, you think about it. Keep your eyes and ears open." She rose and handed me the lunch bag, which I dropped in my wastebasket.

"Back to the mines, as they say."

I wasn't really annoyed with her remarks. "Baffled" would be a better description. I sat quietly, fingering the jade earrings I wore every day. Green is for go? I wondered.

In a short time I had the recovery unit so thoroughly inventoried no one had the nerve to even snitch a paper clip. My strength had increased, my blood pressure was back to where it should have been and, best of all, Stallings said it would be all right for me to undertake some patient care. That was the work I loved most. A good nurse is accepted no matter what she looks like. And acceptance, God knows, was what I needed.

I concentrated on meeting the needs of my coworkers as well as my patients; dwelling on other people's problems helped me to take the focus off my own. My worst moments were in the evening when I was alone in the apartment. Gary and I had never had another conversation, from the moment we tacitly agreed that the marriage was over. I envied him his ability to lose himself, to numb pain with beer. I'd wonder where he was, if he was all right.

Whenever I felt despair getting an upper hand, I'd go to Dr. Stallings' office. He always seemed glad to see me but for the life of me I couldn't pick up on the "vibes" Daria had mentioned. He was always kind, his low measured voice always steadied my nerves. He didn't seem to mind if I just sat quietly in the chair and watched him come and go, or listened to him as he handled phone calls. I knew I was soaking something up from his healing presence, his vitality, his unfailing compassion for every patient. It was a contagion I desperately needed.

Best of all, he seemed to understand my need to be there. In the safe space of Dr. Stallings' office I could not think of myself as grotesque, as an object of revulsion. There were actually times when I even felt like a perfectly normal woman and would walk around with my head held high—until I'd catch sight of myself in a mirror or window. Then my spirits would plunge and I'd return to the safety of Stallings' office. But each time I went back, I wasn't quite as low as the last time. And though I continued to plunge when I saw my reflection, I didn't plunge quite so far.

"It's exciting, Leo," Daria said as we walked to the parking lot.
I looked at her.

"Watching the new you emerge, the one I always felt was there, the one you didn't need until now. I like her a lot. Thought I'd just let you know."

I thumbed my nose at her and hopped into my car. I gave a brief toot of the horn as I backed out.

"I didn't say you were a saint!" she called out before getting into her own car.

Driving home I thought about what she'd said. A new me. Maybe. But was that person real? God, if only I could sit down and talk to someone about all the feelings that were churning inside. Had the old me been real? Was it just a careful veneer? I had so many questions. I had never thought about my identity before, I had just taken it for granted. What you saw was what you got. Now all that was changed. What attracted people to me, Velveteen Rabbit that I was?

I flipped on the lights in the apartment, vaguely aware that something was different. Then it dawned on me: the small stack of cardboard cartons containing Gary's things were gone. He had come in while I was out and taken them. Knowing I wouldn't find him, I looked anyway. The living and bedroom were both empty. I hung up my coat in the closet and then performed my nightly ritual of whipping up "dinner" in the blender. My heart felt like a lead weight. I poured my pureed "dinner" into an oversize glass, plucked a straw from the jar on the counter, and walked to the living room and flipped on the TV.

As I sipped the liquid, I realized that to some extent I was changing. There really were resources to draw on. I really didn't know if Dr. Stallings would succeed in his effort to build me a new face. All I did know was, mangled or not, I had to be real.

Nor did I try to delude myself that my appearance would ever be as it once had been. But with Stallings' encouragement I had begun to build some confidence that one day someone might look across a room and think, "Oh, isn't she interesting looking." Not beautiful. I'd be happy to settle for interesting.

Thanks to Stallings, I believed that day would eventually come. And the best thing about it would be being able to speak. I had had five months, now, of grunted gutturals and lockjawed whispers.

"Don't confuse Stallings with God," Daria warned me. "He's a mortal man and one with a problem. Something more than snow tires."

I'd noticed it, too. He was obviusly preoccupied, walking around like the proverbial absent-minded professor. I had even caught him fitfully dozing at his desk on a few occasions.

"Of course," Daria went on as she popped a pickle in her mouth, "it *is* March. He could have a heavy stake in the ice-break sweeps."

The ice-break in Alaska is always momentous, and not just because it means spring has come. It happens all at once, unpredictably, sometimes in the dead of night when everyone is asleep. It sounds, as one old-timer put it, "like the opening guns at Verdun." Bets are placed in advance about the day, the hour, the minute.

"On the other hand," she wiped her mouth daintily with a paper napkin, "it could be something else. What do you think?"

I shrugged and dropped my malt into the trash basket. Then I reached for the slate and wrote, "I think tomorrow I'll try vanilla."

"You've got it." She rose and waddled to the door, her back erect as only a very pregnant woman's can be.

As it happened, the ice-break coincided with the monthly hospital staff dinner meeting. The dinner was compulsory and a predictably deadly bore. But it did beat sitting at home alone in front of the TV. Green crepe-paper streamers across white tablecloths, the intersections punctuated by African violets in plastic bowls. They had gone all-out. Everyone knew it was a ceremonial dinner because the chef put sauce on the chicken—chopped onions, frozen orange juice, canned cherries and brandy. The general's aide gave a speech summing up the general. The general gave a speech summing up the month's progress: the casualties flowing in, many victims of our own napalm, others victims of Southeast Asia itself. There were medical problems that weren't even in the books. A new kind of malaria, szi szi gambushi, strange viruses with un-American patterns. And the burns. Always the burns.

The general droned on and on. I was seated at a rear table, as befitted my rank. Major Stallings was seated forward and to my left. I found myself watching him, telling myself it was out of boredom and knowing better. He ate very little of the dinner. He brushed away dessert and coffee. No room for them: he was drawing on the tablecloth! A confirmed doodler myself, I was amused. I often drew coiled springs, falling dominoes, rising smoke plumes—but I had never drawn on a tablecloth. That must be boredom carried to a higher plane. Then, as the after-dinner speech came to a close with everyone rising to applaud, I saw Dr. Stallings do something *really* peculiar.

115

He took a Swiss Army knife from his pocket, neatly cut out that portion of the cloth on which he had been drawing, rolled it up, stuffed it in his pocket, and walked away.

As he passed, he looked into my astonished eyes, patted his pocket and said, "This concerns you, Leo. See me first thing when you get in tomorrow."

I walked out the door and, at that precise moment, Alaska exploded with the arrival of spring. I heard a joyous cacophony of automobile horns, sirens, even fireworks: the ice had broken. At last! Cynical as I had become about Alaskan seasons—they were all deplorable—I went to bed that night with a sharp sense of expectation.

I got to work the next morning, to find a terse message on my desk. *Report. Stallings.* My God, I was early and he had beaten me in. I went to his office, where I found him behind his desk, white-suited as usual, but impatient with our usual cheery exchange of greetings.

"Lieutenant," he said, nodding me to the chair he had placed beside him, "I figured something out at dinner last night. It's been bothering me from the first moment I saw you on that bloody gurney. There's this problem with your upper lip; a good deal of it is gone."

I looked at him in utter bewilderment. Had he gone mad? Of course I knew my lip was gone.

"I've solved the mucosa problem."

I stared at him.

"I've figured it out, Leo." He could no longer contain the joy in his voice. "Just last night! Believe me, I felt like jumping up from the table and screaming 'Eureka!' But, I figure I'm in hot enough water with the general without disrupting his speech."

No wonder he had looked so miserable all this time. He had made a promise he hadn't been sure he could keep.

Now his words tumbled out in that familiar, passionate rush. "You know, it's absolutely incredible, wait till you hear. I can't imagine why I didn't think of it sooner, it's so obvious." As he caught his breath I imagined a drumroll. "I'll do a gynecological tissue transfer!" he announced.

I looked at him, my face blank with noncomprehension.

"I'm going to replace the missing strip of lip with a strip from your vaginal canal. A small strip, you won't even miss it." He smiled. "I need undamaged vermilion mucosa, as you know, and there it is." He grinned at me, then frowned. "What is it, Leo? I thought you'd be thrilled with the news."

I had left my office in such a hurry I hadn't brought the slate with me, I scanned his desk for a blank piece of paper and then drew it toward me. He handed me a ballpoint pen from his breast pocket. I printed the words carefully. "You want to put a piece of my *vagina* on my face????"

"Why, yes, it's absolutely perfect, the tissue will be totally compatible. I think it will work."

I tapped the piece of paper, my index finger beneath the word "vagina."

"Oh," the smile disappeared from his face. "Is that what's bothering you? Leo, it's exactly the same tissue, vermilion mucosa."

I nodded slowly. Then wrote, "Bizarre."

"No, it's not. Do you realize what a breakthrough this will be? It's never been done before and there's no other place on your body that can supply such perfect donor tissue."

It *was* bizarre. Couldn't he see that?

He sighed, obviously disappointed that for once I wasn't on his wavelength. "You don't have to give me your decision now. Think it over. But when you do, remember this: win and we make medical history. Lose, we're disappointed, but you won't be any worse off than you were before."

I winced.

His nose was practically touching mine. "But I think it will work." He said it softly, his breath fresh and warm.

I leaned back, trying to collect my thoughts. The nearness of the man had completely unnerved me.

"Aesthetically it will be good. No one will even know when they look at you."

I rose slowly from the chair and nodded. Somehow we both knew the decision was made.

Once in the hall, I relaxed enough to let my body shudder. The very idea! Who wanted to make that kind of medical history? If it weren't so crazy it would be funny.

A surgeon engaged in anything more innovative than setting a broken leg is bound by ethics to notify his colleagues and the hospital director ahead of time. The reason is quite simple. If the procedure doesn't work, they get some of the flack. The word of Dr. Stallings' plan for Lieutenant Harmon spread through the hospital like a brush fire. He had scheduled the surgery for April 21 and had selected his team. Judging from some of the reactions, it was as if someone had uncovered a plot of Hanoi to bomb Elmendorf.

The medical men were overwhelmingly negative, even Victorian in attitude. The female staff, on the other hand, treated the news with relative aplomb after first raising their eyebrows a bit. The consensus there seemed to be, "Why not? The tissues of the mouth and vagina are similar."

Daria threatened to wash an orderly's mouth out with soap after overhearing a few untoward remarks.

"What did he say?" I scribbled.

"I don't remember exactly. All I know is it was uncalled for."

I looked at Daria dubiously. She remembered, all right. Actually she didn't have to tell me; I had heard a few lewd comments myself.

"You heard the latest?" she asked, halfway through a container of milk. She was trying to quit coffee for the balance of her pregnancy.

I shook my head, not sure I wanted to hear whatever was coming.

"Seems a few of our vaunted senior medical staff marched on the general and made a formal protest."

I raised my eyebrows.

"Seems they want to stop the surgery. Evidently they're very concerned about what the rest of the world is going to think when they hear that Elmendorf, a top emergency hospital of the U.S. military, has performed radical surgery involving the sex organ of an Air Force nurse."

"You serious?" I wrote.

"As God is my witness, it's the bare-faced truth. From what I've heard, a good many of them may require Stallings' services on the lower rear portions of their own anatomy when he gets through chewing them out."

I made a guttural noise, which was in lieu of a good belly laugh. God, how I ached for the luxury of a good laugh, a good cry, either or both.

"Anyway, I wanted to remind you that I'll be in Cleveland on the twenty-first." She tapped the large protuberance that had replaced her lap. "I'm due on the eighteenth. And though I know it may sound strange, this is one time I want to be near my family."

I nodded. I'd have wanted the same thing given half a chance.

She lumbered to her feet and gave me a reassuring pat on the head. "Promise you'll write and let me know how everything goes?"

I nodded and then wrote, "When do you leave?"

"Probably Monday or Tuesday. Depends on when I can get some space on a commercial flight, you know how they are about military personnel."

I nodded and wrote again. "Don't know how I'd have gotten this far without you."

Daria lifted the film on the slate slowly, erasing the words. "Don't worry, they're stamped indelibly on my mind." She sniffed and straightened her shoulders. "Well, guess I'd better toddle—I mean waddle—along. I'll see you before I go so don't get gushy now."

I waved her off as she tried to plant a kiss on my head.

The days that followed can only be described as tense. I saw Stallings each day, at his desk, in the wards, doing his job. His resoluteness seemed to make him taller. Aspersions cast on his sanity, sincere expressions of concern that the operation might fail, that he had no right to use me as a guinea pig—all were received with the same grave bow of acknowledgment and no verbal response whatsoever.

Daria delivered a ten-pound boy twelve hours after arriving in Cleveland. I wrote her a congratulatory letter and included some of the details about what had been going on.

Meanwhile, my other friends on the hospital staff were dubious at best. As the day of reckoning approached each of them took me aside at one point or another.

"Think it over."

As if I hadn't.

"What if it doesn't work?"

It's worth a try.

"Get another doctor."

I couldn't think of another doctor that would have shown the care or gone to the lengths that Stallings had. Now that he was being ridiculed at every turn, I wasn't about to walk out on him.

Some of the scrub-room comments were vile. One surgeon had even gone so far as to suggest I might suffer all sorts of embarrassment when I menstruated. Only he didn't phrase it quite that nicely.

I was finally summoned before the general.

"Lieutenant, I think you know that I am opposed to Dr. Stallings' plan for surgery on the twenty-first."

I nodded.

"You know that there is an alternative procedure?"

I nodded.

"Will you consider it?"

I shook my head. The alternative procedure had been considered and the general no doubt knew all about it. Dr. Stallings could take a less controversial patch of skin, from my thigh or my stomach. Of course it would not be red, as a lip should be, and because of sweat glands and hair follicles it would be less attractive. Not only that, the transfer of skin from the stomach or thigh that wouldn't raise a staff eyebrow would leave me with permanent bad breath. Somehow that struck me as a much more unappetizing prospect than did the transfer of mucosa.

"All right, I can see your mind is made up." The general clearly was not at all pleased. "Dismissed."

I wanted very badly to apologize for posing such a public relations problem. Instead I simply saluted and left his office. It was hard to believe that a hospital as sophisticated as Elmendorf would be in such an uproar over a simple skin graft that probably wouldn't take forty-five minutes and posed no risk whatsoever to the patient.

CHAPTER 11

Dr. Gills now stepped authoritatively into the picture. He insisted on a careful gynecological examination.

"Well, Leo. I'm happy to tell you that the tissues in the vaginal canal are healthy and strong."

I scribbled quickly on my slate. "Will I be able to have children?"

"Absolutely. Removal of tissue will inhibit neither your capacity for bearing children nor your sexual capacity. I quite approve of what Stallings is doing and shall assist if he wants me to."

On the slate. "Wish you'd tell him that."

"I'm sure he knows."

Again the slate. "Don't assume anything."

"It's been that rough?"

"You *know* it has!"

"All right, Leo, I'll speak to him. I guess a word of encouragement never hurt anyone, even a Young Turk like Stallings."

I left Dr. Gills feeling elated. If the obstetrical-gynecological department chief approved of Dr. Stallings's innovative surgery, everybody else might as well shut up. I headed directly for the office that had become my haven.

"Ah, Leo," he smiled. His voice was hoarse with fatigue.

I leaned over his desk and scribbled the good news from Gills.

"That's great. Now maybe we'll be able to enjoy some peace and quiet."

And sure enough, we did. A welcome calm settled over the hospital.

A few days later Dr. Stallings showed me the crew roster for the O.R. on April 21. Three surgeons—Stallings, Gills, and Dr. Sessions, as backup. Two surgical nurses, one a captain. Two instrument nurses. Local anesthesia again—my contribution. The fewer drugs in my system, the better.

"Are you sure about the local?" Stallings asked quietly.

"Are you kidding?" I wrote. "You think I'm going to miss the most controversial operation ever performed in Alaska?"

He laughed. "You really are something special, Leo. I don't know if I've ever told you that."

For once, I was glad I couldn't speak.

On the evening of April 20th, I was so excited I needed a heavy-duty sleeping pill. Tomorrow we were going to write medical history. At least, Stallings would. I knew it without the slightest trace of doubt. The knowledge was exhilarating. How I wished Daria could have been here to share the victory. She had asked me to be godmother to little Bob, her son, in absentia. I had agreed, and she'd arranged for someone else in Cleveland to stand in at the church for me. And now she had sent me a telegram. I pulled it from the envelope and read it again: LOVE AND LUCK TO YOU TOMORROW. THAT M.D. YOU'RE INVOLVED WITH IS THE BEST AND SO ARE YOU. LOVE. DARIA.

What did she mean, "That M.D. you're involved with?" Maybe the operator had garbled the message. No, the more I thought about it the more I realized that was exactly the message Daria had intended. Boy, would I give her hell when I could speak!

If she were here she'd help me with an inspired idea, I'd walk into the O.R. in the morning in a silky green peignoir. That would give the hospital gossip mill some grist!

As it turned out I was actually wheeled in wearing a green hospital nightie after being administered a good solid shot of a drug that leaves you in a suspended state of being there and not there at the same time. I was floating above it all.

I signed an agreement to the surgery, noting with some surprise

122

that it had also been signed by Gary: *Gary Cox, 101 Bunnell Street, Apartment 1C.* So that was where he was living—well, well. Sergeant Blackwell, the instrument nurse, firmly wrapped adhesive tape around my wedding band. One of these days I'd have to take it off. I had long since removed the opal "friendship" ring Gary had given me in that sawdust-strewn bar so long ago. "Opals are the gem of tears, unlucky." I could hear my grandmother's voice as clearly as though she were standing next to me. No tears for me, Grandma. Not any more. And no one could be luckier than I am right now. Look at this team assembled here. There isn't another like it in the world. They're about to do something that's never been done before.

Patient floating. Ring is taped. Ready, Dr. Gills. Ready, Dr. Stallings. The voice seemed to be coming from a great distance.

Just as Stallings had predicted, the procedure was brief. In fact, considering the simplicity of the whole thing, it's surprising it took as long as it did. My own theory is that both surgeons were nervous and exerted the utmost caution every step of the way.

Stallings did indeed make medical history. The mucosa transplant is now known as the Stallings procedure. It fills all of one paragraph in *Plastic and Reconstructive Surgery,* Volume 47, No. 5:

> Lip switch operation with Fleur de Lis mucosal graft from upper lip to lower lip and vaginal mucosa graft to upper lip. The vaginal mucosa was inserted and sutured in place with 4-0 chromic catgut. Estimated blood loss 50 cc's. The patient tolerated the procedure well and left the operating room in good condition.

No mention is made of the months of anguish, the resistance, the courage and commitment it took on everyone's part. There it is in all its brilliant simplicity. Nothing to it. Not unlike putting a new sole on a beat-up hiking boot. No mention was made that I had become even more grotesque than ever. The tissue hung lividly on my lip. Eventually it would be trimmed. For now it looked as though a ghastly mistake had been made. And again, my mouth was sutured shut. I was imprisoned in silence once more.

"Good news, Leo," Dr. Stallings said as he finished up the post-op examination. "The transfer tissue took. Now we can start planning the second stage. Doing anything on May 13th?"

I nodded.

"Really?" He seemed taken aback.

"Have date with you." I wrote.

"Oh, you had me worried for a minute."

I studied him casually. He looked pale and tired, I wondered what he did to relax. Daria had once joked that he was the sort of man who was happiest working and found relaxing hard work. I could sympathize with that. My worst moments had been at those times when I'd had nothing to do. I had very nearly slipped over the precipice into an abyss of paralyzing depression. I might have, too, if it hadn't been for Stallings. Now he became conscious of my gaze and looked at me expectantly. I hastily scribbled a question. "How soon after 2nd stage can I talk?"

He thought for a moment. "It's hard to say."

The second procedure on May 13 was termed "second-stage lower lip reconstruction with revision of vermilion, upper and lower lips." It took an hour and a half. Another strip of vagina was split and the vermilion now was spread evenly and artistically across my upper and lower mouth. I had lips again. My actual thought was that a man might even risk approaching me with the lights on. Looking in a mirror as soon as I was out of the recovery room, I saw that my new mouth was better than the old one: The lips were slightly fuller. Something I had always wanted while growing up, a truly sensual mouth. I snorted.

"What's so funny?"

Stallings had poked his head in.

I pointed to my mouth.

"You don't like it?"

I nodded as hard as I could without disturbing the sutures.

"Well, I'm not sure I do."

I sat bolt upright.

"Don't worry, I'm not talking about anything drastic. But if you like this, I can hardly wait for you to see what I have in mind. We're going to rebuild your jaw. Then you'll be able to talk. And I have the feeling you'll talk your head off. I want to hear all about you. In the

124

meantime, come to my office. I have a surprise. Reserve about an hour."

I loved that "reserve an hour." As if I had a busy social schedule.

As I opened the door to Dr. Stallings' office I was enveloped in the sound of the lushest music I had ever heard. He was poised on a low stool before an elaborate stereo system that gave forth music quite unlike anything I had ever heard.

"Pretty good, huh?" He grinned. "It's quadraphonic sound, the next best thing to being there." He pressed a button and a tape cassette ejected neatly out of a slot. "Eight tracks, that's what gives it the dimension." He inserted a second cassette. "Listen to this." He turned and faced me.

It must have cost an absolute fortune. I wondered if he had one at home too. He probably did, he and Anita probably listened to classical music together. As the music washed over me I gradually began to understand. He liked popular music! Anita was into classical. At least that was how I imagined her, a walking encyclopedia of every symphony and concerto ever written. She probably frowned on "Mr. Tambourine Man" and the artistry of Buffy Ste. Marie. To my untrained ear they sounded beautiful, and they were certainly to my taste. His too, apparently. I sat content in my chair and absorbed the music. Then, as the *pièce de résistance,* he played the old Fred Astaire number, "A Foggy Day in London Town."

When the tape had finished we sat absorbing the silence. "Ever been to London?" he asked finally.

I shook my head.

"Stick with me long enough, Lieutenant, and you'll go places you've never dreamed of. Guess what we're going to do to start the new year?"

I waited for him to explain.

"We're going to open your mouth!"

I started to more or less cry. New Year's Day was seven months away. Was that why I was crying? I wasn't sure. This incredible man was instilling an excitement in me for the future, for what lay ahead. I was riding high on the wave of his enthusiasm. Whatever the reason, I cried. Some briny, mucal mess went down my trachea and into my chest. I choked so hard on it, Stallings had to pump it out.

He was holding me, Fred Astaire was singing again ". . . the sun

125

is shining everywhere." Stallings held me until the spasms subsided, then he gave me a glass of ice water from the thermos on his desk.

"Shucks," he said, "I thought you'd be happy."

I nodded that I was; he nodded that he knew I was.

He took my hands in his and I saw that he had noticed the absence of my wedding ring. I don't know what became of it; I'd simply taken it off and it had somehow vanished.

In the months that followed, I slipped into a comfortable routine of work. The high points were those moments I spent in Stallings' office. Obviously he felt as comfortable as I did, which pleased me very much. We had become a team and had developed a highly sophisticated level of communication. In the beginning it had startled me when he would comment aloud on something I was thinking at that very moment; now, I was used to it. I didn't mention it in my letters to Daria, not wanting to invite further expansion on her "vibes" theory. I told myself that Stallings and I were two pros working toward the same end, that what was happening to us was perfectly natural under the circumstances. And—no matter the paradox—the circumstances were, after all, extraordinary. It was hardly surprising that I needed to be in his presence, that just being with him had a healing effect.

Other than an occasional movie with Nurse Susan, my social life was nonexistent. I didn't mind. Nor did I try to contact Gary, even though I now knew where he lived. We both needed time for our wounds to heal. The marriage was over, even though we had yet to begin, let alone finalize, formal divorce proceedings. Time. Everything would come with time. I was learning all about time, thanks to my enforced silence. I was also learning patience, patience with time, with life itself.

When I thought of Gary and me it was without resentment or bitterness. If anything, I felt a sense of poignancy. How silly and shallow I had been! Worried, at twenty-two, about being an old maid. Attracted to Gary, in part, because he was the sort of person my family would never, ever have permitted me to date. And hell-bent, as Stallings had seen, on changing him.

Not that he hadn't meant what he had said about wanting to settle down, wanting to change. I had taken that at face value. Just as he had taken me at *face* value. He had believed, as I had, that I would make a good wife. Neither of us had any idea what we were letting ourselves in for; any real knowledge or acceptance of each other as we were.

I thought about Dr. Stallings. We were so similar in temperament, I wondered if he had gone into marriage with the same naive outlook I had. Some of the thoughts he shared with me seemed to bear out this theory, though he had never once mentioned anything about his home life. I hoped it was good. I hoped that his wife comforted him and cared for him and fed him emotionally. He gave so much, his needs must be great.

Now I was beginning to sound like Daria! I decided to stop romanticizing, even though it was a common enough phenomenon between patient and doctor. I was keenly aware that my life, my future, depended on this man. Of *course* I would love him.

I pulled my thoughts back to Gary. What had been the key factor in my deciding to marry him? He needed me, pure and simple. And I had gone overboard trying to meet that need, done too much, tried too hard—all of which he had resented. Anyone would have.

I knew that a good many people on the Base had rejected Gary because of his inability to cope with my disfigurement. I wanted so much to talk with him, to tell him it was all right, that I understood. I couldn't. My lips were literally sealed.

I "discussed" it with Dr. Stallings via slate.

"If people weren't so hard on him, it would be better."

"I know, Leo. I could feel the man's pain when I spoke with him about the mucosa transplant."

"I wish I could speak. There's so much I want to tell him."

Dr. Stallings assured me that the time was drawing near. He had scheduled the jaw reconstruction for January 5.

"Won't undo anything," I wrote slowly.

"No." He agreed. "It's important that you understand that."

"Just hate to think of him suffering."

Dr. Stallings looked at me long and hard, then reached for the phone, which had begun to ring insistently.

127

CHAPTER 12

Dr. Stallings looked up and smiled as I took my seat in the chair facing his desk. An incredibly intense sensation of warmth rushed through my body. Dear God, did it *show*? Come on, Leo, this is no time to start getting crazy. I wondered if the good doctor had any idea how just being in his presence eased the ache in my spirit. Of course he did. That was why he was always so warm and responsive. It goes with the territory; every good surgeon has that ability to soothe, to inspire confidence. And God knows, I'd needed massive doses of that. I still did.

The approach of Christmas filled me with a sadness and rage that I had been forced to bear in silence. I was tired of being alone, even though I knew lots of people were alone, many of them right here at Elmendorf. I was tired of living in a crucible of silence. I was also again in acute danger of falling over the edge into an abyss of self-pity. I hoped Stallings wouldn't notice my state of mind, and knew that he would. He had an unfailing ability to read my thoughts, sense my feelings. He'd had it right from the start. This day was no different.

"What's wrong, Leo?" he asked softly.

I raised my eye from the clutter in my bag and shrugged.

"Feeling blue?"

I nodded, there was no point in denying it. I did feel blue, *very* blue.

He began to talk animatedly about the procedure he was planning for the jaw reconstruction. He was so earnest I was overcome with a desire to sit beside him, lean my head against his shoulder, close my eyes and see the images he was pointing. I wanted to cry in the worst way, but that was something I had never done easily; not since my mother had died when I was small. His voice stopped mid-sentence. He got out of his chair, walked quietly around the desk, and knelt before me. I felt his strong slender fingers brushing the tears that had begun to ooze painfully from my eyes. The flesh on my cheeks tingled.

"Oh, Leo," he murmured, "it won't be long now. I *know* how lonely it's been, how silent. It's all right to cry, it really is." But he continued to brush away the tears as they spilled down my cheeks. "There's a difference between grief and self-pity, don't be afraid. It's all right, it's all right."

I blinked, trying desperately to regain some composure. He wiped my eyes again, then hitched himself up on the corner of his desk. "Just think, by this time next month you'll be talking. No more slate. You know what I'm looking forward to more than anything?"

I shook my head.

"Hearing you speak. I was thinking about that the other night. Here we've been in almost daily contact for over a year and I have no idea what you sound like. I've never heard your voice."

I pulled my slate out of my bag and printed, "Hope you won't be disappointed."

"Leo, nothing you could say or do would ever be a disappointment. And not only will you be able to speak, you'll be able to eat. Think of it! *Eating* with a knife and fork; no more tube feedings, you'll be able to chew honest-to-God food. And I'm going to buy you a dinner you'll never forget. We'll go somewhere really elegant. How about a nice juicy filet mignon for Madame?"

I looked at him blankly. A filet mignon? A real dinner? An elegant restaurant? It had been so long, I could neither imagine nor remember what it would be like to eat a meal out.

He read my eyes and smiled. "What's the first thing you're going to do when you can open your mouth?"

I wrote slowly, "Sing and shout my head off. Call my family. Most of all, tell you how grateful I am for everything."

He walked back to his chair and flipped on the tape deck as he passed. Simon and Garfunkel's "Bridge over Troubled Waters" filled the room.

When you're weary and feeling small, when tears are in your eyes, I'll dry them all. I'm on your side when times get rough and friends just can't be found. He was speaking to me through the music, the lyrics. Come on, Leola, you've been cooped up in yourself too long. This is a married man. Yet the lyrics expressed everything exactly, he must know that. He had minutes ago brushed away my tears. He had been my best friend when my own husband couldn't stand the sight of me. He had been my bridge over troubled waters right from the first moment I saw him. He had lain himself down, over and over again. How could I possibly ever thank this man? There weren't enough words, good enough words, even to express what I felt.

"Now." He was all business, back at his desk. "The jaw reconstruction is going to be a tremendous undertaking, as you know. Unless you object, I'd really like to use a lightweight plastic instead of metal."

"Isn't metal better?" I wrote, still under his spell. If he had said he was going to shape my jaw out of Silly Putty I wouldn't have argued.

"Not really. It might be more impregnable than the plastic but it's heavier and will cause muscle fatigue and sagging, whereas the plastic won't."

"Okay, plastic it is."

"This surgery is going to be pretty rough, I want you to consider a general anesthetic."

"*No!*"

"I thought you'd say that. How about a compromise? A local and some Valium administered intravenously, then you can still keep tabs on what's going on."

I nodded. A Valium drip wouldn't put me out. All it would do is eliminate sensations, not of pressure but of pain.

"Good, I'm glad that's settled. You know, Leo, I'm not going to let you forget how remarkable you are. I don't think I've ever met anyone with your brand of courage."

Courage! If only he knew. I wondered what he would say if he knew how frightened I was of the dark. It was something that had started after the accident. I had to have a light on in order to get to

131

sleep. I had to know where I was, I had to know the dreams weren't real.

I'll take your part when darkness comes, pain is all around. Simon and Garfunkel knew. And Stallings probably did too. He'd understand about needing the light. *Sail on silver girl, sail on by. Your time has come to shine. All your dreams are on their way, see how they shine. But if you need a friend, I'm sailing right behind, just like that same old bridge over troubled waters, I will ease your mind, if you need me to.* Yes, he would understand. He understood everything. He was the most extraordinary man I had ever known, no wonder my pulse raced.

I resolved the problem of spending Christmas alone by working. The patients I attended were not in the least concerned with my appearance. Most of the ones who'd been around for a while knew me fairly well, including all the details of the accident, thanks to the hospital grapevine. Even the newly arrived wounded seemed unfazed by the silent apparition that tended to their needs that day. They seemed genuinely appreciative of the warmth and attention I was able to give them along with the nursing care. In many ways, it was the most rewarding Christmas I had ever experienced.

On January 5th I was prepped and draped in the usual fashion. A transverse submental incision was made in a staggered pattern, downward to the border of my chin. I followed Stallings every moment of the way and longed to be on my feet, at his side, watching the procedure instead of hearing and feeling it as the instruments moved across my flesh.

Next the new periosteum was incised and Dr. Stallings made a pocket for the Silastic chin implant. He sutured that in position and a pressure dressing was applied.

He leaned over, looked into my eyes and said softly, "The patient tolerated the procedure well?"

I blinked.

At last, my jaws were free! My lips, including the portion that had

132

been transplanted from my vagina, also moved and worked. I made a few practice runs with my voice, how strange it sounded in my own ears, not at all the way I remembered it. "Dr. Stallings," I said to the wall, "I'm Leola Harmon."

"And so you are." He was standing in the doorway. "No fair rehearsing."

"I wanted to be sure it worked," I said, embarrassed. "The voice, I mean."

"It's a marvelous voice, Leo. Like a bell. But I expect using it will take some getting used to after being the strong silent one for so long."

"Silent, yes. Strong, I'm not so sure. There were a lot of weak moments you didn't know about. It's probably just as well I couldn't talk."

"Leo, that all went without saying. I knew when you were suffering doubts; and believe me, if you hadn't had them I would have entertained serious doubts about your sanity!"

"You know," I felt awkward and shy, "all I've been able to do for the last year is think of the things I would say once I could speak. And now that I can, I can't think of one single profound thing to say."

"Don't worry, you will. Now about our dinner date, have you given it any more thought?"

"You don't have to take me out, Doctor. A big juicy cheeseburger and french fries would be my idea of heaven."

He laughed heartily; delicious shocks of delight raced through my veins. I had never heard him laugh like that before, it was wonderful.

"My God, woman," he said, "you've got to think bigger than that!"

"The cheeseburger is a noble concoction." I said it with all the haughtiness I could muster.

"And here I am, willing to part with my hard-earned savings." He chuckled. "I'm not often extravagant."

"There's no need for you to be. You've given me so much already, more than you'll ever know."

He looked at me, a long, steady look. "I know," he said softly.

Another electrical charge shot through me. It left me weak, shaken. If he touched me, it would all be over. I'd fall into his arms.

"You know what else?"

I was almost afraid to ask, I felt completely exposed. "No, what?"

"I *like* the way you sound. I like it very much. Your voice is every bit as nice as I imagined it would be."

I looked at him curiously, trying to fathom the idea that he had spent time imagining what my voice would sound like.

"Does that embarrass you?"

God, he's so direct! "A little."

"Well, what about our dinner?"

"Dr. Stallings, it really isn't necessary. You've done so much for me already."

"Dr. Stallings? I wish you would call me Jim. I kind of figured you were already doing that. But then, how could I have known? There's so much about you I don't know, so much we have to get caught up on."

"All right," I said softly, "but won't your wife mind?"

"No."

"I'm afraid I don't know any of the fancy restaurants, you'll have to choose."

"I don't either, but I'm sure I can find one. How's Friday?"

"Friday's fine, I have no other plans."

I telephoned Daria in Cleveland before calling home.

"God, Leo, I can't believe it's you! About time, isn't it?"

"Sure is."

"How are you making out with that doctor of yours?"

"It depends on how you mean that, and knowing you as I do, I know how you mean it."

"That's Leo, all right. Well, tell me! I can't stand the suspense another minute."

"There isn't anything to tell, really. We have a very close doctor-patient relationship and that's all."

"I warned you before I left that God-forsaken place, he seems *very* involved with you."

"And I told you what I thought of that."

134

"It's true, all right. You just won't allow yourself to see it. He *cares*, Leo."

"I know he cares. But it's not the way you think."

"Well, that's not the way I see it. And I'm a pretty good student of human nature."

"Maybe, but on this you're just imagining things. Obviously you've forgotten how I look. It may be years before I can look at anyone without seeing them cringe at the sight of me."

"Good God, Leo, haven't you discovered yet that there's more to you than a face?"

"Of course I have. I just think he loves the challenge I present and the fact that he can do something about the mess I was in."

"How about you? What do you feel?"

I was glad we weren't having the conversation in person—she would have seen through me in an instant. "I have the utmost respect for him as a man and as a surgeon. I think he's a bloody genius and that I'm damn lucky he was here."

"Hmmm. So, everything is working? How does the mucosa transplant look?"

"Better. It needs more work, there's scar tissue in the mouth area and my upper lip still lists to the right. I still have a long way to go."

"I wish I could be there to celebrate with you."

"I wish you could too. How's the baby?"

"Great, just great."

"Give him a kiss for me."

"I will. What did your stepmother say when you told her what's been going on?"

"I haven't called yet."

"For God's sake! Why not?"

"I wanted to try my voice out on you first, my pipes are still a little rusty."

There was a pause and for a moment I thought we had been disconnected.

"Leo, you have to tell them," she said finally. "They have to know what you've been through. Think how you would feel if you were in their place. Do it, don't be afraid."

That was it of course: I was afraid.

I procrastinated on calling Circleville for another day. My stepmother was terribly hurt that I hadn't written them the truth.

"There wasn't anything you could do, Mom. I didn't want to upset you. I had to be sure I was going to be all right."

"Are you all right now?" I could hear the apprehension in her voice.

"Yes. I'm still not much to look at, but a few more operations and I should be as good as new."

"A few more operations? My God, what—"

"It isn't as bad as it sounds. Plastic surgery is always done in stages, Mom. You know that."

"I do?"

"Sure you do."

"Maybe your father and I should come up there?"

"No, it really isn't necessary. I have a wonderful doctor, he may be the greatest plastic surgeon in the world."

"And you have Gary," she said. There it was, the moment of truth. I knew I had to tell her.

"Mom, it didn't work out. We're separated."

"Separated? Oh, Leo."

"I'm sorry, I really am."

"Well," she sighed, "it certainly sounds as though you've been through a lot."

"It's going to be all right and I'm sorry to be telling you this all at once, I know it's a lot to absorb."

"It is. Promise me you'll never do that again."

Do what again? Lose my face? Get married? I gritted my new plastic teeth carefully. Stay calm, stay calm; if she detects the slightest bit of remorse or pain she'll catch the next flight to Anchorage. I wasn't ready for my family to see me. Not yet.

"Don't ever keep us in the dark like that," she continued. "We're your family, we love you."

"I love you, too. And I promise, I'll call from now on."

I studied my face carefully in the mirror and suddenly felt apprehensive. While it was a vast improvement over what had been greeting me in the mirror over the last year, I was definitely no day at the beach. Could Jim really be serious about wanting to be seen in public with me? Could he possibly know what he was letting himself in for? The pitying stares, not only for me, but for him at being stuck with me. Having seen what that had done to Gary, I frankly didn't want to go through it again.

Of course, it was true that Jim didn't see me the way anyone else did. I knew that when he looked at me he saw what I was *going* to look like: not the face I had, but the face those extraordinary hands of his were going to create. But what if being with me outside the environment of Elmendorf changed that view of me? I sighed. I didn't want his peculiar vision destroyed, yet somehow I knew it was a risk I'd have to take sooner or later. What I didn't know was why.

CHAPTER 13

Dr. Stallings leaned back with a pleased smile on his face. "Go ahead, try it."

I gingerly moved my jaw. It worked.

"See if you can rotate it."

"It moves!"

"Was there any doubt in your mind that it wouldn't?"

"At times," I confessed. "It seemed too much to hope for."

"That's understandable, all things considered. Want to take a trial run?"

"You mean chewing?"

"How about a cheeseburger for lunch? Are you free?"

I nodded out of habit. "I mean, yes. Yes, I'm free."

He leaned forward and placed his fingers on my face; his touch dissolved the tension that had been knotting in my stomach. "Good. Let's go, then."

"Now?"

"Aren't you hungry?"

Hungry. If he only knew! Images of cheeseburgers had been dancing through my head for months, but now that the moment had finally come, I was afraid.

He rose from the chair, walked to his office door and waited for me.

"Of course we still have our dinner date," he said as I passed him and stepped into the hall.

It was all I could do to keep from taking one of everything as we passed through the cafeteria line, even the puddings and Jello looked enticing. Jim insisted on paying the cashier. "You can treat some other time."

We carried our trays to an empty table and I stared down incredulously at the food on my plate. This was *my* lunch.

"It's going to get cold, Leo. Go ahead, take a bite."

I could feel his eyes on me as I carefully lifted the cheeseburger to my mouth, opened wide and took a bite. The pleasure was so intense as I chewed and swallowed it that it took a few moments before I became conscious of the noise; a mounting roar from somewhere behind us, cheering and applause. I looked around, bewildered. It seemed as though half the people I knew on the Elmendorf staff were there, giving me a standing ovation.

"This is a great day, Leo!" Nurse Susan called from across the room. What could I do but take a second bite? More cheers. It was the most delicious thing I had ever tasted.

Jim just grinned while I chewed. "How is it?"

"Fabulous, just fabulous." As I ate each french fry, I knew that never again would anything taste so exquisite.

When the last morsel was gone from the plate, Captain Laura stood and tapped her glass with a spoon. On cue Susan emerged from the kitchen bearing an enormous chocolate cake ablaze with candles. I clapped my hands like a delighted child as she approached.

"It's not my birthday," I said as I stood before the flickering candles.

"Make a wish, make a wish," little Michael called as he navigated his electric wheelchair toward me through the tables.

I drew a deep breath, closed my eyes and prayed—that my lips would work well enough for me to blow the candles out.

Another cheer. I opened my eyes. I had done it! They were all extinguished.

"Speech! Speech!"

I looked around the room at each familiar face and knew that tears were streaming down mine.

"What can I say? Each of you has helped me along the way. I'll never be able to thank you properly, but I *do* thank you." I sat down abruptly while more applause swept through the room.

"Cut the cake," Michael whispered from his post at my side.

As everyone came to the table for their piece of cake, there were hands clasping mine, kisses on the forehead. Now it seemed as though the entire staff as well as most of the ambulatory patients were jamming the commissary.

"Who's minding the store?" I whispered to Jim.

"Skeleton crew. A lot of these people are off-duty."

"And they came here for lunch?"

"Leo, you have no idea how much everyone admires you. They wanted to celebrate."

I couldn't believe it. "People have actually come in *early* to watch me eat a cheeseburger?"

"Was it good?" Michael asked.

"It was the best cheeseburger I've ever tasted, I'll never forget it. Not ever. Or any of you."

"Eating a cheeseburger is being real." He smiled.

"You bet, Michael. That's what made it so good."

He smiled his lopsided little smile and switched on the power on his chair. "I have to go now, I always read to the little kids after lunch."

"Drive carefully." I patted him on the head and watched him zoom across the cafeteria to the door where his nurse was waiting.

"You arranged this, didn't you?"

Jim flushed slightly. "Actually, I didn't. I think it was Michael's idea initially and everyone jumped on it. I hope you don't mind."

"Mind? It was terrific!"

"We still have our dinner date for Friday, right?"

"If you want to. But now it *really* isn't necessary. This was a wonderful way to celebrate."

"I want to, Leo. Just a quiet dinner with the two of us, if you feel up to it."

Actually, the idea made me nervous. It was one thing to enjoy the closeness we had developed right here in the hospital. But I wasn't at all sure I was ready to go out into the outside world, even with Jim

141

Stallings. I also wasn't about to disappoint him, not now, not after all we had been through together.

"Of course I feel up to it."

I didn't see much of him during the day that Friday. We had a busy schedule in the O.R., a new batch of wounded had arrived from Viet Nam and even I was kept running most of the day. There wasn't time to build up much anxiety about my impending venture out into public. Late in the afternoon I began to fear that he might decide to cancel the dinner date, that he would be too tired. Especially after such a long day. I checked my hair; the set had held well. My face, while a huge improvement, was still nothing to get excited about. I stood back and eyed myself in the mirror. I was presentable.

The phone on my desk rang and I jumped.

"Are you ready?" Jim asked.

"Yes."

"Meet me out front, in about five minutes?"

"All right." My heart was knocking against my ribs. Come on, Leo, stop making it such a big deal.

He was standing at the entrance looking like a nervous first date. "Do you want to follow me in your car?" He asked as I neared him. "Or shall we go together in mine?"

"We'll have to, I gave mine to Bugler for servicing. I hope that isn't an inconvenience. He's dropping it off for me in the morning. I hope you don't mind."

"I don't mind a bit." He smiled and held the door open for me. We walked in silence to the parking lot.

The *maitre d'* gave a slight bow, "Ah, Major Stallings, table for two." He drew a neat line through Jim's name on the reservation list, his face registering not the slightest trace of emotion. I wondered if Jim had been here before. It looked like a very expensive place. The *maitre d'* signaled to a captain, unhooked the velvet rope and told the captain to take us to table seven.

I was grateful for Jim's reassuring nearness as he followed me. I kept my eyes riveted on the captain's back, looking neither right nor left, determined to avoid the stares if there were any. Someone had once told me that if you act as though you look good, you'll look good. The captain pulled the table forward in one fluid movement and I slid onto the curved leather banquette, my heart pounding wildly. This was a crazy mistake. I should have insisted on a pizza in some dark, dingy place.

Jim's knee brushed mine as he slid onto the seat, then the table was gently repositioned.

"May I suggest a cocktail?" the captain asked in a perfectly pleasant voice.

"What would like, Leo?" Jim asked as he straightened his tie.

"What are you having?" My voice sounded shaky.

"Well, ordinarily, I don't indulge, but since this is a really special occasion I think I'll have a martini."

A martini. That's big-league stuff. I wondered what the folks at home would think if they could see me now? Probably think I'd gone to hell in a handbasket. Drinking martinis with a married man and a damned attractive one at that.

"I'll have the same," I said keeping my chin lowered.

"Two very dry vodka martinis," Jim announced to the captain, patiently standing by.

So far, so good. I hadn't heard any gasps as we threaded our way across the dining room. If people had been upset by my appearance, they were far too civilized to let it show. Still, I couldn't bring myself to risk looking around the room. What if someone *were* staring and whispering? I focused my attention on the perfect arrangement of tea roses in the center of the table.

Jim sighed. "You don't know how I've been looking forward to this."

"Me too," I lied.

A waiter arrived with the martinis and served them silently. Jim lifted his drink, his hand cradling the glass. I followed suit.

"A toast," he said. "To us and all the good things to come." His voice was soft and his eyes were looking directly into mine as he took a sip of the clear white liquid.

Just like a lover in the movies, I thought as I returned his gaze.

Good grief, Leo, you're acting tiddly and you haven't even tasted the drink yet! I took a cautious sip of the icy liquid and felt a surprising, delicious stab of warmth all the way to my toes.

"You look wonderful," he smiled.

You don't look so bad yourself, Major. I suppressed a giggle. My God, this stuff is lethal!

"Thank you," I murmured as I took a small second sip. "This is really delicious."

"It is good."

I chanced a peek around the room; the rest of the people were engaged in their own conversations, no one was paying the slightest bit of attention to us. I let out a long, slow breath, the tension easing out of my body. Just relax, Leo. Have a nice time with this nice man.

"This is the best martini I've ever tasted," I announced. He didn't have to know it was the *first* I had ever tasted.

"You know," he said slowly, "I feel a little nervous."

"You do? Why?"

"I feel as though I'm on a first date and not sure of what I'm supposed to say or do."

"I feel a little strange myself."

"*How* strange?"

"When we first sat down, I thought I was drowning. Almost the way I was feeling the very first time I saw you, only then I really was drowning."

"In the Emergency Room?"

"Yes. I knew I was in shock. I could tell by the color of my nailbeds that I was already cyanotic and anoxic. It was terrible. I felt as though I was swimming underwater, my lungs were bursting for air, and I knew I couldn't make it back to the surface, it was too far and I just didn't have the strenth. No matter how hard I tried, I kept sinking deeper and deeper. I was dying, and I knew it. Then I heard what sounded like a shot and in you skidded."

"The door must have hit the wall. You had one hell of an airway problem, I could hear it all the way in the hall. And then there was that idiot worrying about your teeth."

"So it really was like that?"

144

"Yes."

"I wasn't sure if it actually happened that way, if I was conscious or just hallucinating. You took an awful chance pushing that dentist away like that."

"I realized later that I probably shouldn't have pushed him, he was only trying to do his job. But then it wasn't the sort of situation that allowed time for the amenities. I don't think he'll ever forgive me. In his book I'll always be an arrogant bastard."

"You'll never know how many times I've thanked God that you did come barging in and shoved him away. I wouldn't be here now if you hadn't." I paused and studied his face. "Does it bother you that he thinks you're arrogant?"

"Not really. I'm not running for mayor, I'm trying to be a good surgeon. I think he at least respects me and, if nothing else, is relieved that I did what I did. It wouldn't have looked too good if you had succumbed while he was checking your occlusion."

I chuckled. "He might have had some trouble explaining *that* at the staff meeting."

"Needless to say. But I have to learn to be more tolerant of other people, I realize that now."

I found myself studying his face as he spoke, wondering about the strange sadness that occasionally erased the animation of his features. Something was troubling him and I didn't think it was the dentist.

"I think you have incredible tolerance," I said.

"Not for incompetence."

"None of us should tolerate that."

"That's true, but sometimes I wonder if I'm being too judgmental."

"You're not judgmental. You just have very high standards."

"Would you like another martini?" he asked, looking at my half-empty glass.

"If you're having one, I will. I must tell you, though, I'm not much of a drinker. Especially after that damned drunk hit me and got off with a slap on the wrist. But even before that I never drank much."

145

"Does your family drink?"

"Not at all. They're devout Methodists."

"Tell me about them."

"Good people, hard-working, the salt of the earth. And yours?"

"The same."

We talked about early childhood, his on the farm, mine in Circleville.

"What are you going to do when you leave the Air Force?" I asked tentatively. It was a question that had been bothering me terribly for some time, even though I had been trying very hard not to think too far ahead. The fact was, I couldn't stop agonizing over the fact there would be a time when he would leave Elmendorf. The thought filled me with dread.

His eyes danced. "I've decided already, now all I have to do is work it all out."

I looked at him quizzically.

"Plastic surgery. God, Leo, I can't tell you how much it means to me, everything else is boring by comparison. There really aren't words to describe the feeling, it's unlike anything I've ever known. That's not to say I don't love medicine itself, I do. I always have, from the moment my cousin allowed me to observe him work."

"How old were you then?"

"About fourteen."

"Not many fourteen-year-olds would have been able to handle watching surgery."

He looked at me in surprise. "It's funny, that never occurred to me. I suppose most kids that age would be revolted or frightened instead of fascinated. But for me, a whole new world opened up that day, a world with limitless possibilities."

There was such unadulterated joy in his eyes, I found myself wishing I had known him then.

"What's really strange is that I was sure—really sure, even then— that I'd not only be a surgeon but be a terrific one. It was only a matter of time."

"It doesn't sound strange at all," I said. "I'll bet you'd have been willing to skip childhood so you could get started."

"I would have if I could," he said with a smile. "You understand so much, Leo, that's why I love being with you."

The only word that registered for a moment was "love." Leo, it's not a date in the strict sense of the word. You're two colleagues celebrating a major achievement and that's all.

"I don't know that I understand everything," I said. "Not completely."

He looked at me intently over the rim of his glass, "You understand as completely as anyone ever could."

"You have a rare gift," I said, awkwardly trying to shift the subject of this conversation away from me. I felt that I was on shaky emotional ground, that I might blurt out something I'd later regret.

"I always knew I had ability, that I had the potential for being a damn good surgeon if I worked hard. Then you came into my life and everything changed."

"Changed? How?"

"The world I could see got even bigger. I was standing on the edge of a whole new frontier. And, Leo, it didn't frighten me at all."

"It sure frightened everyone else," I said.

He laughed. "That it did. But you can't blame them, they didn't see what I saw. I can't tell you why or how, but I *knew* I knew exactly what had to be done. And that I would do it."

"I'm not sure I wouldn't have been standing there paralyzed like the rest of the staff if I had been on duty the day I was brought in."

"No, I don't think you would have. In fact, I'm sure you wouldn't. You're like me, you have the gift. That's why I know I can share feelings like these with you, that you won't think I'm nuts when I say if it were up to me, I'd operate twenty-four hours a day. You're just as excited by the work as I am."

That was true. I was actually looking forward to all the reconstruction work that still lay ahead. But it was more than just the work, it was Jim. I wanted to be with him, to feel the excitement, to share the work. My greatest fear was of the day when it would all be over, when our military service would be up.

"What's wrong?" he asked suddenly.

I shook my head, "Nothing's wrong."

"Did I say something to upset you? Was I being presumptuous?"

I carefully clenched my new jaw. Easy, Leo, take it easy, just enjoy the moment. Stay in the moment, don't think about the future.

"No, you haven't said anything wrong. This is the most wonderful evening I've had in a long time. I guess I'm a little overwhelmed."

"Are you sure that's all it is?" His hand rested gently on mine.

I nodded, unable to speak.

He looked at me thoughtfully and I dropped my eyes lest he see right through me; I couldn't allow that. We weren't playing a romantic scene, we were doctor and patient, not man and woman. I was no longer a woman in that sense and might not be for some time to come, if ever. That was why I had to sleep with the lights on, I had to stay out of the shadows of fear or hope. I had to stay in the moment and know at all times who I was and where I was.

"I still think there's something you're not telling me," he persisted. "There is, isn't there?"

I felt like saying: you don't want to know. Instead I said, "No. You probably know more about me than anyone, including me."

The steaks were served and we ate in silence for a few minutes. "How is it?"

"Delicious, fantastic, out of this world and much too extravagant."

"Now you sound just like my wife."

I felt as if I had been struck. There it was, reality. My fork froze in midair, then I slowly lowered it. My appetite was suddenly gone.

"That was a dumb thing to say," he said.

"Not at all." My voice sounded strange and I struggled to gather some wild rice on the fork that seemed to be going slowly out of control in my hand. "I know you're married, Jim."

"You know what I mean."

Did I? I wondered. He was married all right, but not only to another woman: He had a mistress he was passionately devoted to, his work. We were sitting together because of that passion, because I was part of it, part of his work. Nothing more, nothing less.

I felt relieved when Jim changed the subject. "You know what I want to do?"

I shook my head.

"Try for a residency at New York University Medical Center after I finish at Elmendorf. That is, if they'll have me."

"Why wouldn't they have you?" Yes, New York made sense. All those fine hospitals. And Carnegie Hall, too.

"Every doctor hoping to specialize in plastic surgery wants to do residency there because of Converse. He's the best in the country, if not the whole world. You know what else I dream about?"

"What?" I whispered. I had lost my battle against the future; here it was, staring me in the face. An interminable gray plain, devoid of all life. It had to come sooner or later, and I would have preferred for it to be later.

"You're there with me, Leo. We'll work together just as we do now."

"We'll *what?*"

"Work together. That is, if you want to. I never asked you what your plans were?"

Plans? I had no plans whatsoever.

"I wish you'd think about it." He drew out his wallet and placed some crisp bills on the table. "I've given it a lot of thought. You'd be my research assistant, we'd scrub together."

New York! It was the only thought my head had room for at the moment. As we walked to the door I felt as though I were floating, far above that awful gray abyss that had been yawning ahead.

I sank into the passenger seat of his car and put my head back. This was one moment I intended to stay in. Reality would wait. I closed my eyes and let the pictures come. Research! Scrubbing together! Working side by side! All the wild dreams I'd thrown out whenever they cropped up. And, wildest of all, here we were, together, driving through Anchorage toward my apartment. Should I ask him up? Will he just drop me at the curb? He'll probably just drop me. After all, it is getting late and he does have a home to go to, a wife waiting. Well, I can ask him, no harm in that. He'll probably say no.

"Fifty cents for your thoughts," he said, glancing sideways.

"Why fifty cents? Inflation?"

"I can feel your mind churning, there must be at least fifty cents' worth."

I laughed. "I was just wondering if you'd like to come up for..." I stopped. For what? I'm out of practice, what do women do in this kind of situation? Oh yes, offer him a drink. "...a drink?" I finished lamely.

He was standing outside the car, holding the door open for me. I hadn't even noticed that we had arrived. God, Leo, you're really losing your grip. I fumbled nervously in my bag for the apartment key.

As Jim helped me off with my coat, panic struck. I didn't have any alcohol in the house. Now what? Coffee, you have coffee. That's what women do.

"I told you I wasn't much of a drinker," I said. "But I can offer you a good cup of coffee."

"I'd prefer that, actually."

"You would?"

He slipped out of his coat and hung it in the closet next to mine. Somehow this struck me as an outrageous act of intimacy. I headed for the kitchen feeling slightly weak in the knees and began filling the kettle.

He was standing right behind me as I turned from the sink. He took the kettle from my hand gently.

"Leo, I don't really want any coffee."

His voice was low, he was staring at my mouth with such intensity that my lips started to tremble. This was no clinical look, no professional admiration of a job well done. I knew that look, knew it from years ago. A lifetime ago. It was desire, pure desire. Leo, you must promise yourself to never, ever drink another martini.

I looked into his eyes and couldn't see them; I felt his fingers on my cheeks slowly tracing their way down to my mouth, over and around my lips. A series of feathery shocks swept through my body. I closed my eyes, unable to look at him. His fingers were caressing, parting the flesh they had created, exploring, touching, turning, I felt as though I were dissolving. My mouth was responding, clinging as he withdrew his fingers. Then his lips were on mine. His mouth was like nectar, I couldn't get enough, nerve endings I didn't know I had were responding to every movement of his tongue and I could feel the effect mine was having on him. Now his fingers were stroking my shoulders and mine reached for his neck, tracing the wonderful warmth of his flesh. This is insane, I thought. This can't be happening and I sank deeper, clinging to his extraordinary mouth. No one had ever kissed me like that before, not ever.

He pulled away for a moment. "Leo . . ."

I drew back a half step and looked at him. "Jim. Don't."

He looked hurt.

"Don't say anything. I don't want you to say anything you'll be sorry for."

"All right, I won't." He sounded cheerful. *Cheerful?* "Where's the bedroom?" He led me from the kitchen, to the bedroom, to the bed, and I questioned nothing. I wanted to preserve each second in this moment, hold it, keep it forever. Because this moment, this dream was all that mattered. The dream of a desperate, lonely woman who would never know this kind of exquisite passion again.

As our bodies merged, I was swept on a wave into the center of the dream: I was beautiful! The wave carried me far above the gray plain and out to a sea where there was no horizon, no past, no future. Only now.

I opened my eyes slowly, wanting to stay with the dream, knowing what I would find: The light standing sentinel against the night terrors. But the room was dark. My eyes adjusted slowly; it wasn't a dream. Jim Stallings lay beside me. He raised up on one elbow and placed a delicate kiss on my mouth as if it were the most natural thing in the world. I sighed, the dream hadn't ended, I had gotten my wish. I was still safe in the warmth of his arms. We made love again with an aching sweetness and I lay nestled in the life-giving warmth of his body.

Finally he slipped out from under the covers and slowly began to dress. He tucked his shirt in his trousers, then sat down on the bed and stroked my hair.

I opened my mouth to speak but he stopped the words with his fingers.

151

"Don't say anything, Leo. Let's just take the good things in life as they come."

I sank back on the pillow and watched him as he walked to the bathroom. Amazing. Just amazing. Yes, it certainly had to be a dream, an unusually vivid one. It would last me the rest of my life if I was really lucky. I smiled. Good lord! How will I ever look Jim in the eye on Monday! He'll know right away that he's played a starring role in an extraordinary fantasy . . .

Jim emerged from the bathroom, his hair neatly brushed. But what if it wasn't a dream? What if he really was over there, in the chair, tying his shoelaces? What was I doing going to bed with my surgeon? With *someone else's* husband?

He rose slowly from the chair and slipped his jacket on, then came back to the bed. "I wish I didn't have to leave," he said. He kissed me on top of my head and then walked softly out of the room. I heard tiny sounds: the closet door opening as he removed his coat, the living room light being snapped off. The front door, closing.

I lay quietly on my back, staring at the ceiling. It was real. All of it. It had happened.

"Let me remember this always."

I had said it aloud. Where was he now? Out in the darkness, the headlights piercing the night. What would he say to his wife? "Stop it, Leo." Again the sound of my own voice startled me. Yes, stop it. You've stayed in the moment since halfway through dinner last evening; you can stay there a few hours longer.

I pulled the covers up around my shoulders and snuggled down into the memory.

CHAPTER 14

I didn't see Jim at all on Monday. A busy O.R. schedule followed by a series of meetings kept him tied up the entire afternoon. Nothing unusual about that, I told myself. Then, not two minutes later, I'd be wondering if he was deliberately avoiding me, if he were suffering some terrible remorse over what had happened Friday night.

I longed to talk to him, to reassure him, to let him know—what? That I was making no assumptions that our relationship had changed permanently, had become anything more than a close professional one? No point in saying that, Leo; it's only the way you think you *ought* to feel. You can't make yourself believe it; you'll never make him believe it.

But what if he does view it as a terrible mistake? What then? I didn't want him to feel under any pressure or emotional obligation. If he felt that, we'd lose everything we'd had together up to now—all the closeness, the communication without touching or speaking. The fact was, I couldn't bear that.

I drove home slowly and didn't bother with any dinner. I was more distressed than I cared to admit. And completely alone. I couldn't possibly discuss this with anyone—if even a little bit of the story were to get around, that would turn an already difficult situation into an out-and-out mess. I wasn't about to take that kind of risk. I turned on the TV and settled into an easy chair in front of the screen, not at all aware of what I was watching.

The phone was ringing, the sound had taken a while to penetrate my consciousness. I fumbled for the receiver and said, "Hello?"

"Leo? It's Jim." His voice sounded very far away.

I didn't know what to say, I wished my jaws were wired shut. I finally managed what I thought was a snappy response: "I recognized your voice."

He didn't laugh. "Sorry I didn't have a chance to see you today. Are you all right?"

"I'm fine," I lied.

"Can you be in early, about seven?"

"Yes."

"I think we should talk."

"All right." Surely he could hear the dread in my voice!

"See you then."

I sat listening to the dial tone for a good long moment before returning the receiver to its cradle and myself to the easy chair.

Now knowing what time Jim had called, I had no idea how long I had been sitting before the television screen. It was late; the station had gone off the air without my realizing it. I was staring at a test pattern, my legs horribly stiff. I knew it was not just a matter of having dozed off and waked up stiff. I was terrified, paralyzed.

I tried to move my legs, finally stood up and took a few tentative steps. Got to keep moving, get the oxygen flowing to your brain. Got to think. Got to face whatever comes. Got to face your feelings. Yes. The way you feel is a fact, too.

And just what else is a fact? You need him more than he needs you. That's a fact. You've probably blown it. That's a possibility. You're scared out of your wits. That's a fact . . . I hobbled back and forth, the circulation slowly beginning to pick up in my legs. My head ached.

Trouble with you, Leo, is you don't know *anything*! I kept walking, my legs were stronger, my mind racing headlong toward the most horrible possibility of all: He might want to call the whole thing off. He might suggest I get another surgeon.

I walked to the kitchen, checked the clock. Five A.M. No point in

154

going to bed; I'd never be able to get up in time to make it to the hospital by seven. I put the kettle on to boil for coffee.

I showered, hoping the water would snap me out of my near-catatonia. A fresh cup of coffee, that's what you need. I walked back to the kitchen and poured a cup, brought it to the living room and sat on the couch in my white terrycloth robe, a white towel wrapped like a turban around my wet hair. The coffee was good; maybe it would revive me. It didn't, quite, but I did manage to dry my hair, press my uniform, and get to Elmendorf by six forty-five.

God, I thought, I feel like I'm going to the principal's office. The irony of that struck me. How do *you* know what it feels like? You were never once called before the principal!

"Say again?"

I started with surprise at the new young nurse facing me. Don't mind the lieutenant, she talks to herself, she's a little loosely wrapped.

"Sorry," I said. "I was just thinking out loud."

She shrugged and continued down the hall.

I stood before the door, took a deep breath and knocked. He probably hadn't arrived yet.

"Come in."

Oh God . . . I turned the knob and entered. He was sitting behind his desk. The only illumination in the room came from the small brass lamp that cast a golden pool of light on his hands and accentuated the dark hollows under his eyes. He looked terrible. I wanted to run. I didn't want him to see me cry . . . I walked unsteadily to the chair and sank down.

He leaned back and studied me for a minute. "You look exhausted," he said finally.

"You do, too."

"Couldn't sleep."

I nodded.

"Leo, what happened Friday . . . was probably bound to happen. I've given it a lot of thought. I guess I had reached the point where I couldn't put my feelings aside any longer. I want you to know that I have no regrets, I really don't." He paused again.

155

I didn't know what to say, he sounded so stiff. I kept quiet.

"I also want you to know that if my marriage were good, what happened wouldn't have happened. I don't think it could have. That's been on my mind a lot lately."

"Your marriage?"

"My . . . marriage. I haven't wanted to look at the truth of the situation. But I guess it's over, it's been over for some time and Anita and I haven't been able to bring ourselves to face that, much less make it official. I was very much in love with her when we married and I think she was with me. Even though she knew it would be a struggle, knew it isn't easy to live with a doctor. I think what we had probably started eroding right from the start, only of course we couldn't see it at the time. I think she probably felt that once I finished med school there would be more time. Also she had her own work, her music. She's very gifted."

"Yes, I've heard that."

"I guess I rationalized away the long hours she had to spend alone by telling myself that it was all right, she had her music, she could work on her music. She did, too. I'd come home exhausted, sometimes too tired to eat, let alone talk or hear about her day. When I did talk it was always about my work, *my* dreams. Not that she minded, she really didn't. She always seemed enthusiastic, interested, and I know I must have bored her stiff most of the time."

I started to object.

He waved his hand. "It's different with us, Leo, because you're involved in medicine. It's as much a passion for you as it is for me. Anita would tell me about her music, and while I could appreciate the fact that she was good and the music was wonderful, I don't share her passion any more than she shares mine.

"For a long time that was all right because we both had something we loved to fill our time. But somewhere along the line we began to lose each other. I don't think either one of us was aware of it or could say when it was that it occurred. It happens to a lot of people. When we did become aware of it, we tried to take more interest in each other's work. I'd go to concerts with her, sometimes I'd fall asleep, I was so tired. When I was at home in the evenings, I had to study and she felt she couldn't practice. It's the little things that undo a marriage, not the big ones. The small daily acts of indifference that create

156

the distance. And there is distance, Leo. A lot of distance that's been there for a long time.

"Anita and I dealt with it by working harder at our respective careers, and as far as anyone could tell we were two well-adjusted young people who were really on their way, accomplishing all sorts of good things. It was so wonderful-looking, we actually believed it ourselves and excused the lack of closeness, or ignored it, or both. I don't think either of us could really look at what was happening. We always felt that eventually it would work out, that the time would come when we would be close again . . ."

His face was filled with such sadness—here, surely, was the source of that fleeting expression I had noticed over the months. I wanted to reach across the desk and comfort him. Instead I continued to sit there in the chair, motionless.

"Leo, do you think I'm rationalizing?"

"No, I don't think so." I thought about Gary and how hard I'd tried to share my feelings about my work with him. How frustrated I felt when he clearly showed his lack of interest. "People rationalize when they're afraid to look at the truth. I think it takes courage to face that kind of reality."

He nodded slowly. "Yes. I could see that with you."

"With me?"

"When you went home, against everyone's advice, to be with your husband. It was obvious that the gulf between you two was too deep, too wide to ever be bridged. I knew that was the reality you'd have to face."

"Why didn't you say something at the time?"

"I was tempted to, and then that old cliché, 'Physician, heal thyself,' popped into mind. I knew I would do the same thing myself even though I also knew my prognosis wouldn't be any better than yours. The whole thing upset me a lot. On your behalf, but also because it made me look at myself—and that was something I now realize I had been avoiding. I was working longer hours, taking on more responsibility than I needed to just so I wouldn't have to let what had happened to Anita and me break through."

"I can understand that. I was doing the same thing until the accident happened and brought everything to a head."

He leaned forward. "That's it. Sometimes it takes a cataclysmic

157

event to make us look at reality—*shake* us into looking at it, really. You had the accident, it brought the problems of your marriage to a head. Otherwise, you both might have gone on for years without knowing what was wrong. What's worse, you might never have known until the better part of your life was gone."

His eyes were intense and I knew he was talking about himself as much as he was about me.

"You're right," I said. "Painful as it has been to lose Gary and our dreams of a life together, I think it was better to find out now, rather than waking up some day at seventy and realizing the whole thing had been a dreadful mistake."

"It happens, Leo."

"I know it does. Then there are times when I'm alone and I miss him terribly and wonder if we might have been able to work everything out."

He nodded. "I guess that's the trap. You keep telling yourself that it will get better, that soon you'll have more time or more money or a better job or another city to live in, and then it will all change and become what it should be. But the fact is that all the while you're telling yourself this, you've been growing further and further apart."

"Have you talked this way to your wife?"

"More than once."

"And?"

"You know what happens, one or the other of us gets defensive. We still have a lot of feeling for each other."

"And now you feel guilty?"

"I think I've felt guilty for a long time, a sense of having let her down in some important way, of not being the sort of man I should have been."

I shifted in the chair; my nerves were ragged from lack of sleep and I wanted more than anything to go off to an empty room and climb into a bed and escape into a deep, dreamless sleep.

He leaned back in his chair; his face was unusually pale. He was exhausted too.

"I haven't been one of those husbands who has run around having affairs. That would have hurt her too much, and frankly I haven't had the time. But I realize I might as well have been having affairs, because all my passion was going into my work. Anyway, we have been doing some talking lately, not just over this weekend but for the last couple of months. Sort of feeling our way around all of this, being careful to not say anything we'll regret later. I think that's important, don't you?"

"Yes." I was fighting exhaustion, practically nodding off as he spoke. Would this conversation never end?

"When I invited you to dinner, I wasn't planning a seduction scene. I hope you believe that."

My eyes flew open. I was wide awake.

"I've known for some time that I've felt . . ." he searched for the words, ". . . really strongly about you. I kept telling myself in the beginning that what I was responding to was your extraordinary courage. Then as I began to envision what I could do for you, I got carried away by the vision. Still, I kept telling myself that *all* my different feelings for you were natural under the circumstances, that as time went by and we got the major portion of the reconstruction out of the way, we'd just settle down into a nice friendly professional relationship. Instead the feelings continued to grow and I had to start looking at them whether I wanted to or not. You knew I was troubled about something, didn't you?"

"Yes."

"Yet you never asked, why?"

"I don't know. Maybe I couldn't face my own feelings."

"Why?" His voice was very gentle, but very insistent.

"Same reasons as yours. I kept telling myself that of course I would feel some special connection, you were giving me back my life, restoring me to the world. When Daria said maybe it was something more than admiration or gratitude, I became very angry with her."

"Daria said something?" He was genuinely surprised.

"Yes, before she went home to have the baby. She said she sensed something between us. I got mad, or scared—or both."

"Why?"

"It struck me as being sick. I mean, what in the world would you want with the likes of me? I looked like an escapee from a mad scientist movie, someone no man in his right mind would even want to get near. I thought Daria was insensitive even to mention it."

"What did she say?"

"She said I was wrong, that I had a hang-up about external beauty, no sense of what really made people—made me—attractive."

"She was absolutely right."

"I didn't think so at the time. Yet I couldn't help myself, either. I had to be near you, it was as if I were drawing the courage and comfort I needed from your presence. You sensed so much—did you sense that?"

He shook his head. "I was always happy to see you, I always felt better when you were here. You were so interested in the work we were doing and even when you couldn't speak, we were communicating. That's it, of course!"

"What is?"

"We communicate, even without speaking. Anita and I never have, not on that level. That's like nothing I ever experienced before. Which is why what happened Friday seemed so natural, so right. It was like spontaneous combustion."

He was right about that. Just thinking about it sent waves of heat through my body.

"The fact is," he continued, "Anita and I have not really been communicating—on *any* level that's important—for a long time, and we're just coming to grips with that and with what its done to the love we once had. I don't think either of us is cut out to live in what so many people seem to accept as 'arrangements' these days. You know, the you-go-your-way-and-I-go-mine sort of thing. I think we care about each other too much to live that way."

So, he was writing me off. Well, what did I expect? I didn't want to be lurking around having an affair either; it wasn't my style any more than it was his. I shivered violently.

"You look like you're about to keel over. Why don't you lie down for a while and get some sleep? I'll be in surgery for a couple of hours, we can talk some more after that."

I nodded. A great cloud of exhaustion was fogging my mind. I couldn't think, not any more. I was numb. He got up, walked quietly to the chair and held out his hand. I took it and marveled at its warmth; my own hand felt as though it had turned to ice.

"I'll put you in the recovery room, no one will bother you there."

I didn't question him, just let him lead me to the bed. He tucked me in the way my father had, night after night, when I was little. "Sweet dreams," he whispered as I sank into oblivion.

I opened my eyes with a start. Where was I? It took a moment for me to realize that I was not in Intensive Care. That had been a dream. But this was real: I was lying on a bed in my whites doing the unthinkable, sleeping on duty. Captain Laura would have a fit if she found out. I sat up and tried to get my bearings, not sure of what day it was, how long I had been there. My uniform was a mess, looked like I had slept in it—which I indeed had. Captain Laura wouldn't like that, either. I slipped from the bed and checked the hall; if I could get to my office unnoticed, I could change there and no one would be the wiser.

As for the crazy dream, I couldn't shake it from my mind. Jim and I were in the Operating Room; I was holding the instrument tray on my stomach as I had held it so often while he made some minor adjustment to my new mouth or removed a scar. I was handing him an instrument; the doors swung open and Anita walked in, walked over to the table and announced that she was divorcing Jim and that I had better not contest it. Not if I knew what was good for me. Then she sat down at the operating table, which had a keyboard, and began playing a beautiful concerto while Daria and Captain Laura stood by and applauded politely . . .

"You're going around the bend," I said as I opened the closet door and found a fresh set of whites hanging on the rack. I changed quickly and switched my lieutenant's bars and name plate. I inspected my face in the mirror on the back of the door, I still looked tired but not nearly as bad as I had looked earlier. Amazing what a little sleep could do.

Jim had said a lot and, while nothing was resolved, he had eased my mind somewhat. By describing his own feelings of guilt he had helped to release me some from mine. What was it he had said Friday, when I had tried to say something? "Just let the good things in life happen."

161

Yes, I would do that. Just let the good things in life happen. So what could possibly happen now that was good? I sat down abruptly at my desk and began to cry.

"What's this?" Jim was standing in the doorway.

I reached for a tissue and wiped my eyes. "What's what?"

"I just wondered if you'd like to have some lunch."

"I'm not hungry."

"You should try and eat something. I know I need to, come on, keep me company."

I reluctantly rose from my desk and followed him into the hall.

"Leo, I know it may not seem so right now, but I have a feeling this is all going to work out."

"Based on what?"

He sighed. "I don't know, but the feeling is very strong. Meanwhile, we're going to continue working together, and. . . ."

"Jim. I'm not going to sneak around having an affair with you."

He looked hurt. "I wasn't suggesting that."

"I didn't say you were, but some things are better said. Friday was . . ." I stopped, unable to continue. It was incredible, that's what it was.

"Something very special. At least it was for me. But we really have to go on and try to deal with things as best we can, like two grown-ups."

"Right."

The decision seemed more difficult than any I had ever made. I tried to avoid Jim except when I had something specific to say to him about a case or when we were scheduled for more surgery on my face.

I worked long, hard hours and only occasionally accepted casual dinner invitations from some of the other nurses. They all admired Stallings and would frequently discuss his surgical exploits. None of them so much as hinted that there might be anything more than a close professional relationship between the two of us.

As time went on I began to wonder myself.

I continued to go into work early. Jim would be at his desk, and though I stayed away I knew what he was doing. He always carefully

162

reviewed the anatomy of each patient, the physiology; all the time he spent doing this helped him achieve his results. Sometimes his cosmetic surgery didn't go over well with the Administration, certain representatives of which seemed to feel that so long as the major problems were dealt with, the aesthetic aspects of an injury deserved a low priority—if any at all.

"I don't give a hoot in hell what the Air Force thinks," he said. "I'm going to make this guy as presentable as I can." Then off he'd go to argue his case.

We had become a team. I scrubbed with him at least two days a week at Elmendorf. On Thursdays we'd go over to the Eskimo and operate there. I finally stopped looking for the doctor who had so callously rejected me at their E.R.

It pleased me that Jim and I had truly been accepted everywhere as a team. When Jim would mention our future plans in New York, no one so much as raised an eyebrow; it seemed the perfectly logical thing for us to be doing. One reason was that there was obviously still work to be done on my face, possibly a dozen more operations.

Even Daria didn't come out with any smart remarks when I called and told her that I had made up my mind to go to New York because Stallings was going to do his residency there with Dr. Converse.

If anything beyond that was going to happen, I didn't know what it would be. I no longer even put any energy into speculating as to what it *might* be. I was through with speculating, with dreaming, with hoping. There was one way I could keep my sanity, keep functioning: accept what happened moment by moment, enjoy what there was to be enjoyed while it was there.

What's most important about a relationship, I decided, is not how long it lasts.

CHAPTER 15

"Anita has decided to go home," Jim said softly.

I looked up from the notes we had been reviewing for the day's surgery. What does that mean? The question was a scream inside my brain; I couldn't say a word. Had the very thing I had forbidden myself to think of or hope for actually happened? Was she going for a visit? Was she really *going*?

"Irreconcilable differences," he said. "Two words, they make it sound so simple, so neat."

"Is it that definite?"

"Yes. I have to be honest, Leo, and tell you that I really tried. That in no way diminishes my feelings for you but I had to try, we had thirteen years together. That's not something you just toss away."

"Of course you don't."

"She wants to leave as soon as she can get everything ready for the movers, not that we brought that much up here. . . . It's funny, the stuff you can accumulate."

"I know." *Anita was leaving!* "It could still work out, she probably just needs time."

"No," he said. "Time isn't on our side any more, it's against us. The marriage is finished."

"If it's really finished, then that's not defeat, Jim. It's reality. It takes courage to accept reality—you know that, and you know you did your best."

"Not until it was too late. I still can't help feeling I'm to blame. I neglected her terribly, I didn't try hard enough until it was too late, and that's all there is to it."

Anita was going. My heart sang the news. My face was another matter; with a ferocious exertion of self-control I succeeded in keeping my features impassive.

"Anyway," he sighed, "I hope you can bear with me. We are just going to have to play things by ear for a while."

Who did he mean, "we?" Was he going to make one last-ditch attempt to save the marriage? Was he having second thoughts about having me come to New York? I began to go numb.

"I want you to think about it, really be sure if you want to go through with our plan."

I couldn't keep the relief out of my voice. "I'm absolutely sure."

"Then that much, at least, is settled."

"That much" was only the most I had ever hoped for. I had no right to expect anything other than a close working relationship. I had accepted that. What was important to me was *being there.* Where it would lead was anyone's guess. My greatest fear had been that Jim would change his mind. He was getting out of the Service before I was, and I'd been so afraid that once he and Anita got to New York he wouldn't want me to come. Now she was leaving. She wouldn't be there with him.

I would.

In the weeks that followed, our work schedule was unusually heavy. Jim was operating almost every day, and I scrubbed at many of his operations. It was almost as if the word had gotten out that Dr. Stallings was leaving; more and more wounded patients who required his special talents were being shipped to Elmendorf daily.

From time to time, I was the patient.

"How are you feeling?"

"Good."

"You have time for me to do some work?"

"You're not too tired?"

"Nope."

I'd hop up onto the operating table and hold the instrument tray while he did some of what he called "the fine tuning."

"Do you know how many we've done so far, Leo?"

"I haven't kept score. But, let's see, this must be number sixteen, maybe seventeen."

"We're getting pretty blase, wouldn't you say?" His eyes were full of mischief.

"I suppose we are," I said. "I can just see us still doing this years from now, a little nip here, a little tuck there. I'll be this eternal twenty-two-year old, a female Dorian Gray."

"And everyone will wonder what you're doing with this ancient mad doctor. Uh, Leo, don't laugh, you have to hold still. I don't want to *make* scars . . ."

Occasionally I'd catch sight of a staff member watching the procedure.

"What do you suppose they think when they see you working on a nurse in full uniform?" I asked him.

"God only knows. I guess it looks more than strange to anyone who doesn't know what's going on." He held the instruments away from my face while I let out a subdued chuckle. "Okay, now, hold still just another minute or two and we'll be done for today."

It was fun, it was friendly, it was comfortable. But occasionally our eyes would lock with that intensity I had felt in the kitchen on the night of our "celebration." I would hold my breath until the moment passed. Sometimes I felt as though we were both hanging in suspended animation for hours on end; yet in reality I knew only seconds had gone by. The experience would invariably leave me shaken. Something was there all right. So why didn't he follow through? Time was running out. He would be discharged soon.

What did he feel? What did he see when he looked at me? I peered at the face that was emerging, the face he was creating. Was that it? Was he in love with his own creation? That could happen, I knew; artists often became obsessed by the images they were creating, fell in love with them. Jim was certainly an artist; my face was living testimony to that.

And what about me? What did I really feel? Was I in love with his power? Did I feel awe? Respect? The answer was Yes. Was there

167

anything wrong with that? The answer was No. Was I absolutely sure? The answer was, always, I don't know.

"Leo," I lectured the image in the mirror, "you ask too damn many questions. Why can't you do what Jim said and just let the good things in life happen?"

Even though I was well aware that his discharge was imminent, it was still a shock when it became final. We were sitting in the cafeteria. When he announced that he would be leaving Anchorage, I was suddenly overwhelmed by a feeling of utter abandonment. I tried to fight back the panic.

"What's the matter?" He leaned forward.

"It's nothing. Go on. You were telling me about New York."

"Well," he said, "I'm not sure I know how to ask this . . ." He quickly scanned the neighboring tables to see if anyone was listening, then lowered his voice and said something I didn't catch.

"I'm sorry, I couldn't hear what you said."

He smiled, checked the tables again, then whispered, "I just propositioned you."

"You did? Sorry I missed it!" My voice sang out.

"Shh!" He put a finger to his lips, then quickly removed it. "I don't want the whole base to know, they don't suspect a thing and I'd like to leave it that way. Why don't you come by my office later, I don't feel comfortable talking here." He picked up his tray and left before I could answer.

It was all I could do to keep from running after him; to hell with whether he felt comfortable talking in the cafeteria. I concentrated on finishing my coffee in an effort to keep from bolting for the door.

"May I join you?"

I looked up at Nurse Susan, standing before me with a tray.

"Of course." Rats. Now I was going to be stuck. It's okay, Leo. Calm down, you'll find out what's up soon enough. He said it was a proposition, that means—

"So what do you think?"

Susan had been talking animatedly, I had no idea what about. "The problem isn't that I don't want to have an affair with him," she went on, "it's that I'm not so sure I can handle it."

"If that's the case, then why not wait?" Surely that piece of advice

168

couldn't cause any harm. "I know that's hard, I know how lonely it can be up here. But what do you have to lose?"

"Of course, I'm terribly attracted to him. I've been feeling so confused, I just had to talk to someone. But you're right, what do I have to lose by waiting just a little longer? You're being a great help, Leo, really you are!"

A great help! I'd hardly heard a word she said. Here was Susan who had nursed me through the worst days of my recovery, always there, always attentive, never saying a word to anyone about Gary's behavior, and now I was too self-absorbed to pay attention to her very real emotional distress. That isn't like you, Leo.

"It's a hard decision," I told her. "I don't see how you can really make it until you feel sure."

She sighed. "I guess that's what's been bothering me."

"What?"

"You know," she smiled shyly, "calculating everything. I've never known how to do that. I always envied people who could; but let's face it, Leo, I'm not the Jezebel type."

Her face was shining sweetly; no, she wouldn't make a good temptress.

"Susan, you don't have to worry . . . to feel that it's now or never. Or that it's him or nobody. You're very attractive, the right man will come along."

"Oh God, I'm so sick of hearing that. When? When is he going to come along?"

"I don't know, all I know is someone will. In the meantime, be careful you don't settle for second best. Sometimes it's hard, especially when we're all so far away from home. But remember one thing, none of us is going to be here forever. What you have to ask yourself is whether or not what you can have with this man is really good. Sometimes it's better to just let the good things in life happen and see where they take you."

She looked at me gratefully. "Thank you. I don't know what I'll decide, but I feel better already."

"I didn't do anything, but I'm glad you feel better." I picked up my tray and left the table. I wondered what she would think if she knew she had just unburdened her heart to someone who hadn't even

169

heard who she was involved with. I would have to make it up to her before my time to leave Elmendorf came. She needed a sounding board, a friend. Everyone did. I longed to see Daria, to sit around and discuss what was going on with me and Jim. She'd understand my fears. She might be able to give them names, which was more than I could do at the moment.

I tapped on the door. "Come in," Jim called.

"Are you free?"

"You bet." He hung up the phone. "I was just talking to the lawyer."

I looked at him quizzically.

"About the divorce. I guess you know what that's like."

Actually, I didn't. Gary and I hadn't gone beyond filing for a legal separation. It was something that should be resolved soon but I had been putting it off.

"I'll be leaving on the twenty-sixth, that's a Monday, and I had hoped we could spend the weekend together. Now it turns out I have to be in Seattle for a conference."

My stomach lurched. "Before the twenty-sixth?"

"Yes, that same weekend. I can't get out of it, either. I've already tried. Here's what I was going to propose."

I looked at him feeling that I had lost track of this conversation.

"You come to Seattle too," he said. "That way we'd have the weekend, or most of it. I can put you on the plane back here and then fly directly on to New York."

"I can't just take off for a weekend in Seattle." My God, that was the same offer Gary had made as come-on, a weekend in Seattle. We'd never done it, of course.

"Why not? A change of scene would do you a world of good and it would help me."

"How?"

He grinned. "It would make leaving you a lot less painful."

"But what will people think?"

"Do you really care?"

I smiled. "No, not really. I was concerned for you."

170

"Don't be. Besides, I doubt they'll think anything, they're so used to seeing us work together they'll just assume you're in on the conference too. I don't think you'll get any flak when you get back."

"Won't you be tied up in the conference?"

"A few hours each morning, that's all. We'll have the rest of the time to do as we please. Will you go? Say yes."

"Yes."

Anticipation of the weekend helped ease the pain of knowing that Jim would soon be thousands of miles away, that I would have to finish out my enlistment without him. How would I manage those long, lonely months? I would gather as many moments together with him as I could, like a squirrel storing acorns for a long winter's hibernation. The moments, the memories would see me through. And Seattle would add a lot of moments to my store.

I shopped for the first time in years—recklessly, giddily, smiling at sales clerks like a bride-to-be. I was buying a trousseau, no doubt about it. Lacy lingerie, a dressy dress. Who knew? We might go out to dinner and certainly we wouldn't want to wear our uniforms. My God, it had been such a long time since I had thought of myself as a woman instead of a gentleman and an officer. It was a heady experience and I bought more clothes than I could possibly wear in one weekend. I wanted to look beautiful for Jim.

We left Elmendorf on Friday the 23rd in a military transport. I could barely contain my excitement as we settled into our seats and prepared for take-off. I had no clearer idea of what lay ahead than I had had as a nineteen-year-old wide-eyed Air Force flight nurse. I'd had no fear then, no notion of what was waiting for me. It had all been a grand adventure, I was a healthy, pretty girl ready to take the world by storm.

"I can feel your mind going a mile a minute," Jim whispered as we roared down the runway.

"I was remembering the naive kid who flew in here a thousand years ago." We were airborne; I looked down at the expanse of snow dotted with gray and white rocks. Those must be the mountains, the Chugach Mountains. Somewhere down there was Tudor Road . . .

"You know," he said as he settled back into his seat, "I think I once saw that naive kid when I first got to the base."

I stared at him. "You did? How come you never told me?"

"Well, I'm not completely sure. It's just a vague memory of a pretty, auburn-haired young nurse, full of herself, not a care in the world."

"That was me."

"Not that anything was wrong with that. I think I gave you an appreciative glance, the way I would any attractive young woman, and went on about my business."

"I noticed you too, then someone said you were married and I never bothered to look again."

"Why would you give me a look in the first place? Weren't you married too?"

"Well, yes. But it was a game I'd play."

"Used to being admired?"

"I suppose so. I never went through an awkward stage growing up. You know, worrying about how you look, that sort of thing. I always liked what I saw in the mirror and so did everyone else. I never was introspective, never looked at myself as a person."

"It's an important part of growing. I wasn't blessed with your kind of self-esteem as a kid, I was overweight and very awkward."

"You?"

"Me. I was always hungering for something, I never knew what until I discovered surgery. Then my life changed and without my even trying, I began to trim down to what you now see before you."

"I can't picture you heavy."

"Well, I was. You probably wouldn't have even noticed me. Or given me a second glance if we had met back then."

Shared moments, confidences, another morsel to store away. Jim Stallings, awkward and overweight. It just didn't seem possible. He had a lithe, well-toned body. I had assumed he was a star athlete, a big man on campus, not just big.

Our hotel room was airy and pleasant. Jim tipped the bellboy as soon as he placed our bags on the luggage rack and waved him out the door before he could finish enumerating the hotel services. Jim

172

pulled the DO NOT DISTURB sign from the doorknob and hung it out in the hall. Five seconds later we were in each other's arms, our mouths hungrily tasting, nibbling, fusing. Items of clothing were strewn all over the room. Our lovemaking was wild and uninhibited, exultant beyond anything I had ever experienced. I couldn't believe it, yet I knew it was true: he wanted me as much as I wanted him. We were in a state of enchantment, there was no world outside that room, no need for dinner or wine or small entertainments and distractions. We didn't leave the room until the following day.

Jim was up and out before I awakened; a note was propped on the telephone. "How about lunch around two? Will call soon as the meeting is over."

It was ten-thirty, plenty of time to get ready. I lay back in bed, more content than I'd ever been in my life. The road to this moment had been long, tortuous—and worth every painful step. I loved and was loved by a man I might never have met had it not been for the accident.

The luggage still sat unopened on the rack where the bellboy had placed it the night before. All my lovely things were still neatly folded in the suitcase.

I dialed room service and ordered some coffee, eggs and juice, then fell back on the pillow and let myself drift again. A knock at the door and the rattle of china galvanized me into action. I flew across the room, pulled a pretty robe from the case, flung all my clothes into the bathroom and closed the door on them. "Just a moment," I called out gaily.

The waiter wheeled a table in. I started to sign the check, then stopped and carefully added *Stallings*. The waiter left without a word, but I had caught the pleasure in his eyes as he had discreetly looked me over.

Jim had kept his promise: I was presentable at last.

I tidied up the clothes, hung them on the shower rod so they could steam while I had my bath. I threw a generous dash of bath salts into the water, closed the door and returned to the table to finish my coffee. It was delicious, everything was delicious.

I sank into the bubbles, relishing the warmth of the water and the

173

fragrance of the bath salts. It occurred to me that I could stay right here, right where I was, forever. The phone rang; I snatched a towel from the rack and ran to the table.

"Leo?"

"Yes, Jim."

"Did I wake you?"

"No, I was in the tub."

"I'm sorry."

"It's okay, I'm glad you called. Besides, I have a towel on."

"I wish I could be there." His voice made me forget I was cold. "I just wanted you to know I was thinking of you. We're on a coffee break. There seems to be a fairly nice restaurant in the lobby, can we meet there for lunch? We can go out of the hotel too, if you like."

"No. The one in the lobby is fine."

"I'll meet you there at two."

"Two o'clock." I said.

"I hope I can last that long. It's hard to concentrate."

"I know." I shivered and walked back to the bathroom, sank into the tub, and ran some more hot water. How had I managed to live so long without this man?

I found an amazing number of things to do in the two hours before I could reasonably head downstairs to meet Jim. It took time to decide what I wanted to wear, put on makeup, fix my hair, re-do my nails. Time to admire myself in lacy underwear just before I put on the blouse that set off a pale blue suit. Finally I removed the DO NOT DISTURB sign, left the room and descended to the lobby. In a conference room somewhere down one of those halls sat Jim, looking serious and thinking what thoughts!

I smiled and bought a newspaper, then checked out the restaurant. It could have been any restaurant in any hotel in any city; it looked fine. I glanced at my reflection in a showcase; I looked very nice. "Nice," I decided, falls somewhere between "presentable" and "pretty." My mouth pulled a little to the right but that didn't bother me. Eventually even that would be gone.

At one forty-five I entered the dining room and asked for a corner table for two. The hostess seated me immediately and I dawdled over a tomato juice waiting for Jim to arrive. I wanted to see him as he walked in.

I folded the newspaper, laid it on the table next to my juice and read the headlines in between door checks. A week from now I'll be alone again, but it will be all right. If I keep busy, the months will go by, and then—New York!

He walked quickly to the table and leaned down to kiss my cheek, as though we did this all the time. Then he spread his napkin across his knees. "I'm *starved.*"

"How's the conference going?"

"I thought we'd never finish."

We both ate big lunches, then returned to the room, which was now in perfect order. Jim took off his jacket and tie, kicked off his shoes and stretched out on the bed, his head propped on the pillows. He beckoned for me and I snuggled close to him, listening to the steady rhythm of his heart. We slept without stirring for two hours or so; I awoke with my face still nestled in the curve of his neck.

I sighed.

"Happy?" he asked.

"Very. I wish we could be like this always. I wish tomorrow would never come."

"I know. But tomorrow and tomorrow and more tomorrows and then we *will* be like this."

"Shakespeare?"

"No, Stallings."

He accompanied me to the airport. I was missing him already and I hadn't left yet. We had spent most of the night awake—making love, holding, holding on, and talking. We talked of New York—he would find a place to live, I would join him as soon as I was discharged. We talked about how we would keep in touch.

"Money is going to be tight, I won't be able to call as often as I'd like."

"It's all right, I hate the phone anyway."

"You do?"

175

I looked away. "What I hate is hanging up. At least a letter can be read over and over again. Will you write?"

"Every chance I get. Will you?"

"Every day."

Other passengers were assembling at the gate; the moment had finally come. I wanted to press my body against his, cling to him, never let go. Instead I rose, adjusted my uniform, and put out my hand: "Thank you, Major."

He returned my handshake. "My pleasure, Lieutenant. Have a safe flight."

"Thank you." I lifted my flight bag, turned, and boarded the plane. Very good, Leola, very professional.

"We are starting our descent from forty thousand feet. We should be landing at Elmendorf Air Force base in about thirty minutes, a little ahead of schedule. We have a friendly tailwind."

CHAPTER *16*

I awoke with a start, feeling disoriented, not sure if it was morning or night. That was the trouble with Alaska; it was either one or the other most of the time: in the winter always dark and, in the summer, just the opposite. I peered at the alarm clock under the lamp that burned constantly during the dark months. It was morning all right, the alarm would be going off any second, time to get up. Time. How I dreaded it. My God, how will I get through?

Keep busy, that's how. God knows, there's plenty to do before leaving for New York. A letter home explaining my plans. My stepmother had been urging me to come back where I would be lavished with love, attention, and good food. I'd have to tell her, nicely, that I had to get on with my life, that I was by no means an invalid, that there were still a few more operations to go through.

There was Gary. I would have to call him, arrange a meeting if possible and discuss a divorce. There was work: I needed to start preparing my long-term patients for my departure. Yes, there was no lack of tasks to fill up the days and weeks ahead.

Gary answered on the first ring.

"Hi, it's me." I felt very awkward. "How are you?"

"Leo! I'm fine, is anything wrong?"

"No, everything is fine. I was wondering if you'd have some time to get together. We should talk."

"Sure, I was thinking the same thing."

"Want to grab a bite somewhere one day this week?"

He hesitated and I knew what was going through his mind. Would this be another bad scene?

"Sure, Leo. We can do that if you want to."

"I do. How about tomorrow?"

"Tuesday? Sure. Where?"

"Any place you like."

"How about THE GOLDEN NUGGET? Food's not bad there and it's cheap."

"That's fine. Seven o'clock okay with you?"

"You can call me at the hospital during the day if anything comes up and you can't make it."

"I'll be there, Leo." He sounded relieved. I was too, for that matter. It was time. Time to settle everything. Let him go.

I felt much better and made myself a quick bite of supper. It wasn't any fun cooking a whole meal for myself; I'd either have to psych myself up to do it anyway or at least make dinner dates with other nurses if I didn't want to waste completely away. It would help pass the time.

When I walked into THE GOLDEN NUGGET Gary was already seated at a table in the darkest corner. I waited a moment, took a deep breath, and sailed across the room.

He almost knocked his drink over as he stood. "Leo, you look great! You really do!" He meant it, too. His eyes were filled with disbelief.

I shrugged, then sat down, "I'm a long way from being there yet, but it is better."

The admiration in his eyes was open. "Better than better. I would never have believed it was possible." Then he flushed. "I guess that was a lot of the problem, I didn't believe it was."

"I know. I had some rough moments myself."

He nodded, took a sip from his drink. Then, catching himself, "How rude, I didn't ask if you wanted anything."

"Just a club soda." My mouth was dry.

He signaled to the waitress and ordered a club soda.

178

"You have something too," I said.

"No, this one is fine. I can't get over it, I just can't get over it."

"I'm glad you like it."

"I do, very much. You look really terrific," he said shyly.

I wanted to laugh, he was making me nervous, disarming me with that ingenuous charm of his.

"I guess I know why you're here. The divorce, right?"

"Right."

The sadness in his face made him look older than I remembered him. "I haven't wanted to face it," he said, "but it really will be for the best. I kept wanting to pull myself together and be a better man about . . ." he shrugged, "everything."

"I think you've been better than most men would have been under the same circumstances."

"That's not true. I couldn't handle it, that's a fact."

"Well, it's nothing to beat yourself over the head with. We made an honest mistake, that's all. It happens to lots of people."

We discussed terms. I wanted the break to be simple, clean. No alimony, no reason for him to keep on resenting either of us. He wanted me to reconsider.

"No. Please let me have my way in this, it would make me feel better."

"You really mean that?"

I nodded. "I've given it a lot of thought."

"So have I. That's why I want you to have something from me. I want you to know how sorry I am. I want to make it up to you."

"It's not necessary. I *know* how sorry you are, how hard you tried. That's what counts."

"All right." He paused for a long moment. "You want me to take care of it?"

I had hoped he would say that; it might be important to him some day. One less act to regret. "Yes, it would help me a lot if you would."

"Then I will, don't worry about a thing."

We had dinner and talked like old friends. He was filled with plans for his future: *his* plans, not the ones I had been making for him.

"And what about you?" he asked as he stirred his coffee.

179

"I'll be going to New York. Dr. Stallings is there, he'll finish up the reconstruction and at the same time I'll be working with him as his scrub nurse. At least, that's the plan for now."

"You really think a lot of him, don't you?"

"Yes, he's a great surgeon. I don't know what would have happened if it hadn't been for him. I shudder to think."

"Are you in love with him?" His voice was timid. Then he took my hand. "Don't answer that. It was a dumb question. I wish I had had his talent, I wish I could have been the one to do something for you."

"Gary, you *have* done things for me. I'll always remember you and the great times we had."

He insisted on paying the check and we walked out of the place together. No heads turned, we were just a nice couple going home.

He held the car door for me and leaned toward me as I put the key in the ignition.

"I guess this is goodbye, isn't it?" His voice was soft.

I looked up at him and nodded. He offered a weak smile, then bent down and planted a kiss on my forehead.

"I'll never forget you. And Leo, please drive carefully."

He closed the door and stepped back. I drove slowly out of the parking lot; in the rearview mirror I watched him watching me leave.

I felt light, calm. Free. If I'd known *this* was what "goodbye forever" was going to be like, I'd never have put it off so long.

The time passed more quickly than I could ever have imagined possible. I discovered that, like Jim, I had the ability to lose myself completely in my work; and while the nights were long I didn't exactly feel lonely. I wrote him every day and read his quick scrawls over and over again.

He had found a small apartment in Washington Square, he hoped I would like it. Converse was brilliant, he loved the work they were doing. He couldn't wait for me to be there.

Every night, before going to bed, I carefully drew a line through the date on the calendar that had just passed. All the details of my life and departure were neatly in order. Soon I would be leaving. Soon I would be in a new world, a world where I had no past, where there

180

would be no basis for comparison or sympathy, no reason to hide my feelings for Jim from other people. Or from myself.

Captain Laura arranged a surprise farewell dinner. It was held in lieu of the mandatory staff meeting, otherwise I would never have showed up. I had insisted that I wanted to just go, that I couldn't bear saying goodbye to all the people who had sustained me over the years, especially those I had grown close to.

The room was festooned with balloons and streamers, music was blaring through the PA system and a bar had been set up along one wall. Even the general seemed jolly, and when his time came to make a few remarks, he actually seemed at a loss for words. His awkward beginning was greeted by enthusiastic applause. Then he leaned over and planted a boyish kiss on my lips and the room went wild. Anyone would have thought Hanoi had just surrendered, that the war was over. The tumult was joyous, everyone's face was shining except mine. Jim should be here to share in this.

I focused my eyes on the table where he had sat at that long-ago staff meeting, sketching the surgery that would change my life.

"And now," the general concluded, "we have a special moment, the one we've all been waiting for."

I felt like a sleepwalker awakening in panic. Was I going to have to make a speech? Then, through the hubbub, I heard the steady hum of little Michael's wheelchair as it approached the head table. Captain Laura and Nurse Susan flanked him, each carrying a guitar. A hush fell on the room as the two women began to sing a haunting folk song I had never heard before. Their voices were beautifully matched, Captain Laura's a rich alto and Susan's a clear sweet soprano. Little Michael proudly held a shiny triangle which he played with precision, the clarion sounds hanging in the air like notes from a delicate silver bell. It didn't matter who saw my tears. I was as grateful for the tears as for the haunting music. These were my people, I wanted them to know how deeply they had touched me and knew no language was adequate to communicate the depth of my feelings.

Kennedy Airport . . . a clump of people at the gate. Would Jim be there? My flight from Seattle had been delayed three hours—

181

equipment trouble. I had nearly gone mad with impatience. If Jim wasn't able to meet the plane, our contingency plan called for me to take a taxi to the apartment and let myself in with the shiny new key he had mailed me three weeks earlier. I had stored the key carefully in a little leather coin purse Michael had made for me in occupational therapy.

If I'm not there when you step off the plane, I'll be home as soon as I can. *Home.* New York? An apartment I had never seen in a city I had never dreamed I'd visit, let alone live in?

"Leo!" His voice came from somewhere in the crowd and then I saw him.

I broke away from the line of passengers funneling into the terminal and flung myself into his arms.

"Let me look at you," he said stepping back and holding me by the shoulders.

"I'm something to look at, all right. Dirty and tired and rumpled. I was afraid you might not be able to meet the plane."

He enfolded me in his arms. I nestled, tired and happy.

"Come on," he breathed, "let's get out of here before I do something that will get our pictures plastered across the front page of the *Daily News.*" He picked up my hand luggage and circled his other arm comfortable around my waist as we walked to the baggage claim.

We jounced and bounced in a battered yellow taxi over what felt like a rutted, washed-out country road.

I tried to steady myself. "Aren't there any tires on this thing? It feels like he's driving on the rims."

"Potholes," Jim explained as we careened onto the Triboro Bridge. "Look, Leo. There it is."

I followed the direction of his arm and caught my breath—New York! Spires and towers reaching for a black sky. And somewhere, in the middle of all that, our apartment. Our future.

The apartment was tiny. A studio, which translates as one fair-sized room with an alcove containing a sink, small stove, and toy refrigerator. The bathroom was barely big enough to turn around in.

"It's fabulous!"

"Not much in the way of furniture," Jim apologized.

"This is all we need," I said, falling across the bed.

At some point during the evening we took a shower together. He toweled me dry, then himself. His hair was standing on end.

I giggled. "You look like you've been electrocuted."

"I'm surprised I wasn't."

The sheets were cool and crisp as I settled into his arms. The candles flickered and burned, giving off spicy scents until they extinguished themselves. I slept peacefully—without a night light.

I awoke to the aroma of fresh coffee. I stretched languidly, then rose from the bed. Jim was at the bathroom sink, shaving. He smiled at me in the mirror, turned, and planted a big foamy kiss on my mouth. We looked at our reflections and laughed; I had sprouted a frothy moustache.

"Well," he said as he poured the coffee, "it isn't exactly the Waldorf."

"I love it. The service here is fabulous."

"I think so too. I wish I didn't have to leave."

"You know you don't mean that. If you didn't have your work, you'd be miserable."

"True. But that's all I've been doing lately, working. I think I'm entitled to a little play too."

I leaned across the crate and pecked him on the end of the nose with a kiss. "You certainly are. We both are. Do you have to go in today?"

"Yes, unfortunately."

"I'll go with you."

"I told Personnel you'd probably be in tomorrow, I thought you might want some time to get settled."

"I'm settled."

I adapted quickly to the routine; it was almost identical to the one Jim and I had established at Elmendorf. We scrubbed together often, I assisted in his research and worked in the surgical ward. We also continued with my facial reconstruction much as we had in Alaska, availing ourselves of the operating room whenever it was free. Dr. Converse was fascinated by his star pupil's work and frequently popped in to see what we were doing.

To augment his income as a resident, Jim worked long hours in the Emergency Room. I enrolled in some business courses in case I might have to take on part-time work. We never did furnish the apartment, knowing we would be leaving New York as soon as Jim's residency was completed. But I felt we needed something to make the place uniquely ours, something special that wouldn't cost much and that could be left behind if necessary.

Because of our tight budget we hardly socialized at all, although we did form an attachment to two interns who were clearly in awe of Jim and his work: Harry Stein and Ray Wilkes, both from out of town, both intimidated by the hospital and New York. We particularly liked Harry because he lived two floors below and lived a life as spartan as ours. Ray didn't come over as often, especially once he discovered the incredibly varied night life New York had to offer. But he did look upon Jim and me as an old married couple playing the role of surrogate parents, and I enjoyed the role enormously, even though we were almost the same age.

"Wow!" Jim exclaimed in the doorway to the apartment.

"You like it?" I asked, getting up from my knees where I had been putting the final touches on the Christmas tree.

"It's beautiful." He closed the door and set the grocery bag he had been carrying down on top of a crate.

"See how it is with the lights on." I plugged them in and stood back.

"Our first tree," he said softly.

"It's artificial," I said apologetically.

"It is?" He reached over and touched a branch. "It certainly doesn't look it. How do you explain the smell?"

I spritzed the air with an aerosol can. "It's all an illusion."

He kissed me fiercely. "The hell it is."

"Can you do me a favor?"

"Sure. Want me to make dinner?"

184

"No." I handed him a glittery angel. "Can you put this on top? I can't quite reach."

He gently placed the angel on top of the tree. "There! Now it's perfect."

Long after Christmas had passed, we still had the tree up. We had no place to store it, but the real reason was that we loved it. It was the one thing we'd added to the apartment. We lived around the tree, ate in front of it, made love by it. It spread its enchantment over everything we did and we told each other we weren't being childish, that it was fun to come home to.

I found a better-paying job in the Cardiac Unit at Columbia Presbyterian Hospital. I missed working side by side with Jim, but knowing that we were saving and building for a future made the long days bearable.

The following December Jim learned that he would be taking a two-month hospital rotation in England, exchanging with a British plastic surgeon. I spoiled our last few days together before he left; I was feeling too sorry for myself to enjoy them.

"You could always come with me," he said.

"We can't afford it. Besides, Daria is coming. Maybe we can go to England some day for a vacation, right now it would be silly to spend all that money."

"How long will Daria be staying?"

"I'm not sure. She and Bob are visiting his parents on Long Island. We'll probably all have dinner or something."

I was bored, irritable, and at loose ends while Jim was gone. It didn't take me long to realize that this state of mind was at least partly the result of our having lived in near-isolation. I hadn't made any friends; there wasn't anyone to call for a quick dinner. And while the looks some of the interns gave me were flattering, I wasn't about to encourage any advances.

I was beginning to suffer depression for the first time since the early days of my recovery, and I disliked myself thoroughly. Daria didn't arrive a moment too soon.

"My God!" She stood transfixed in the doorway. "I can't believe my eyes. Bob, look at this!"

He kissed me on the cheek. "You look wonderful," Daria said as she plunked herself down on a carton. "So this is the love nest. I like your tree."

"Would you like some wine?" I asked shyly. "I'm afraid that's all I can offer."

"Wine is fine."

I poured two glasses.

"Aren't you having any? After all, we must have a toast."

I poured a third portion into a jelly jar. We clinked our glasses in a toast, then Daria pulled an envelope of snapshots from her purse.

"Your godson."

I admired the photographs; he wasn't a baby any more. My God, the time had gone fast.

Bob had made reservations at the Four Seasons, ignoring my references to the many delightful restaurants close by that would be less expensive.

"This is a special occasion. Besides, we've always wanted to go there. You'll be doing us the favor."

As the fountain tinkled in the background we filled each other in on our lives.

"I simply can't get over it," Daria said as she finished dessert.

"It was superb," I said.

"Not the mousse, silly. You. I knew Stallings was good, I didn't know he was a miracle worker. This may sound strange to you, but I honestly think you're more beautiful now than you were."

"She's right," Bob added. "I can't put my finger on it."

"There's something in your face that was never there before—" she held up her hand as I started to speak—"no pun intended. I know exactly what you were going to say, but please, Leo, remember we are in mixed company." She gave Bob a look. "No, I mean it. There's a glow about you, of course, but there's also something in your face that is, well, *arresting*."

I didn't know what to say.

"Have your folks seen you yet?" Bob asked carefully.

I shook my head.

"Well, you can take that off the worry list," Daria said. "They aren't going to go to pieces. Now tell me, I want to hear all about you and Stallings."

"Jim."

"Yes, Jim."

I told her of his plans to open a practice in Des Moines, Iowa; of the work he was doing with Converse; his work in England, mine in the Cardiac Unit.

"Sounds terrific. You going to Des Moines with him?"

"Yes."

"When's the date?"

"Probably not until the spring, we'll probably leave separately. I may stop and see the family on my way out there."

"I don't mean when are you leaving for Iowa. When are you tying the knot, getting married?"

I squirmed. "We haven't discussed that."

Daria and Bob exchanged glances.

"Leo," she said, "you're living like two kids in a fantasy world lit by a Christmas tree, eating off packing crates. Don't you think it's about time you started facing a few facts?"

"Easy, Daria," said Bob.

"Well, I don't mean to come on too strong but my God, Leo, you've been through enough as it is. How will it look if he arrives out there, a young single plastic surgeon with a young single female assistant. I mean, Des Moines is *not* New York!"

"I've thought of all that. But I don't think it's for me to say."

"Why not?" They both asked together.

"Well, he's done so much for me already. I just don't think I should be the one to bring it up."

"But if he asks you to marry him, you will?"

I looked at Daria long and hard. Of course I would, it was the thing I wanted most in the world. But he had been burnt once already and wasn't going to rush into another marriage. I was sure of that.

"Well?" she asked.

"I don't think he is ready for that yet. I don't want to pressure him."

A sigh. "Sometimes I think you should have your head inspected. He may need a little push in the right direction. You might have to be the one who suggests it."

"I'd never do that. I just couldn't. I want him to ask because *he* wants to."

"Well, whoever does the asking . . . I'd offer to be your matron of honor but I don't think I brought you much luck the last time."

I bought a steak at the market, fresh asparagus, and a small bottle of wine: Jim's welcome home dinner. He'd be arriving sometime the following day and I unfortunately had to work. I stored everything in the fridge and then dusted the apartment with a feather duster, the tree taking most of the time. It gleamed in happy anticipation.

What if Jim didn't suggest marriage? I made a peanut butter sandwich, sat down and ate it. Daria was right, but I could find myself alone in New York, sharing an apartment like this one with a nurse. I sat staring into space, the sandwich sitting like a solid lump in my stomach.

I stopped and bought some ice cream for dessert on the way from the bus stop, wondering if Jim had gotten home yet. The apartment door flew open and I nearly fell into Jim.

"I heard your keys." He closed the door, kissed me passionately, and started making love to me so fast I had no time to think. Afterward, I cried, glad he was too tired from lovemaking and jet lag to wake up. Why couldn't we stay this way always, happy and young in front of the Christmas tree?

Later I wrapped myself in a robe and started the dinner while Jim showered. I put fresh candles on the crate and was laying out the place settings when he emerged from the bathroom, his hair tousled from the towelling he'd just given it.

"Something smells wonderful."

"Steak. Nothing but the best." How long could I keep my voice steady?

"It's good to be home." He put his arms around me and drew me back against his body.

I wanted to scream. Don't touch me. I can't bear the thought of life without you. Don't touch me. Don't make me need you so. Instead, I said, "I'd better check the steak."

"I'll do it." He opened the oven door. "It looks perfect. Want me to cut it?"

"I'll get the asparagus." I touched my forehead with the heel of my hand. "I didn't make any hollandaise."

"We don't need it." He had placed the neatly sliced meat on two plates. I added the asparagus and then followed him with the salad bowl. He sat on the bed, set his plate down and patted the spot beside him. "I want to feel you close."

I sat obediently on the bed while he made room for my plate. We ate like Romans, with our fingers. "Disgusting, aren't we?" He parted my lips with an asparagus tip. I felt faint. "Wonder what Freud would make of this," he chuckled as I licked his buttery finger.

"Plenty. Stop being so depraved." I tried to straighten up as he came at me with another asparagus. "I want to tell you something."

"Don't talk while your mouth is full, haven't you any manners? Besides," his eyes bored into mine, "I have something I want to say to you."

I swallowed the asparagus spear whole and nearly choked. He gave my back a hard slap. I opened my mouth to speak and he pressed his fingers against it.

"Sssh. Listen to me carefully. I've been doing a lot of thinking while I was in England. Now, Des Moines is a fair sized city, but I don't think they're ready for our wild and wicked ways."

I wanted to get up and run.

"So we'll get married and there won't be any problem. What do you say? Leo, are you crying? What's wrong?" He tickled my lips with another cold, limp asparagus. "Leo, you will marry me, won't you?"

I lifted my chin. "Stop this begging and pleading. I accept."

Three days before we were to leave for Des Moines we took the subway down to City Hall for the marriage license. Wanting more than just a civil ceremony, I had phoned a Methodist Church in the Village to arrange a brief service.

"No sweat," a young man's voice had said on the phone, "we can do it." He gave me the address and asked if we wanted music.

"Anything contemporary will be fine," I said before hanging up.

"You got it. See you tomorrow."

"Are you *sure* this is the right address?" Jim asked as we stood in front of what appeared to be a store front. Café curtains were draped across the window.

I peered through the grimy glass. Folding chairs dotted the room and I spotted Ray and Harry sitting to one side. "This is it, I see Ray and Harry inside."

"Good grief, Leo. It looks like a gypsy fortune teller's."

"Well, should we try somewhere else?"

"No, let's go."

A young man with a beard, caftan, beads, and sandals greeted us. He looked like an illustration from my *Child's Bible Reader.*

"We're here to see Reverend Browne." Jim announced.

The bearded young man made a peace sign.

"You're Reverend Browne?" I asked, weak with the effort of stifling an insane outburst of giggles.

"Right on."

"Well, we are Harmon and Stallings."

The young man led us to the makeshift altar and performed the marriage with an extemporaneous rite whose simple words were oddly touching. Church sure wasn't like this back in Ohio.

After we had exchanged vows, Reverend Browne picked up a battered guitar and sang to us while Jim and I stood awkwardly to one side. As soon as the concert ended, Jim reached over and touched the Reverend gently, slipping a bill into his hand.

The Reverend beamed, pocketed the money, and shook both our hands. His touch was gentle, his smile seraphic. We thanked him and he made a gesture of blessing.

Ray and Harry thumped Jim on the back and gave me a peck on the cheek.

190

"That was the nicest wedding I've ever been to," Harry said.

"Unusual," agreed Ray.

We stood in a little clump on the sidewalk for a moment, then Harry suggested we all go somewhere and celebrate. Ray looked at his watch and said he had to be on duty in twenty minutes. He reached over and kissed me, pumped Jim's hand, and slapped him on the back.

"We're going to miss you," he said gruffly.

Jim nodded.

Ray jammed his hands in his pockets and started walking away. "He has the makings of a really good internist," Jim said thoughtfully.

"It took you to make him see that," Harry said.

"I was probably too hard on him."

"No, you did the right thing. He wasn't really cut out to be a surgeon." Then Harry turned and smiled at us, "Well, what are you two going to do for a honeymoon?"

"We leave tomorrow for Des Moines," I said.

"Doesn't leave you much time. I guess you have to pack."

"Why don't you come up?" said Jim. "We have some wine."

"That tree really is something special," Harry said as he accepted a glass. He was sitting on a packing crate.

"You're the only person to ever set foot in this apartment without making a crack about our rushing the season," I said.

"We hate to leave it," Jim said as he sat down next to me.

"You're going to *leave* it? Seems a shame."

Jim looked at me, then at Harry. "Would you like it?"

Harry lived downstairs, it was a perfect idea. I hated the idea of leaving the tree; who knew what the building super would do with it?

"Gee, I don't know what to say."

"Why not say yes," Jim suggested.

"Okay, I will." Harry held out his glass toward us, "We haven't had a toast yet. To you both," he said. "To the best damn plastic surgeon in the business and the greatest nurse I've ever scrubbed with. May the gods bring you the best."

"I think they already have," I said, smiling over the jelly jar rim.

As we carefully removed the ornaments and set them back in their boxes, I studied each one. It *had* been a magical tree.

Jim took the angel down last. He handed her gently to me. "I think we should at least keep her."

"She's tarnished," I said, cradling her in my hand.

"Maybe. But I like her best of all, I think we should keep her."

Harry came back and Jim helped him drag the tree down to his apartment. I followed with boxes of ornaments and tree lights. Jim suggested we all trim the tree together.

"You want to decorate a Christmas tree on your wedding day?" Harry asked in amazement.

"You want to have the magic, don't you?" I asked.

"You bet I do."

"Then let's get started."

Harry brewed a pot of coffee, and when we had hung the last ornament we all stood back in admiration.

Harry sighed. "It's beautiful!"

"Yes, it is," I said. "What you do is add to it yourself as you go along."

"I'll have to get something for the top, a star or something."

"Yes," said Jim. "The finishing touch should be yours."

"Where am I going to find a Christmas star in April?" Harry wanted to know.

Jim pressed the button and the ancient Otis slowly wheezed to the fourth floor, our floor. "Are you sorry we did it?" he asked softly.

"No," I said. "It's time for us to move on. To leave childish things behind. I wish I could remember that line."

"What line?"

"The one about becoming a woman."

The elevator door opened, he held it back with his hand as I stepped into the hall. "You don't need any quotations, you *are* a woman."

He inserted the key in the lock and opened the apartment door. It looked shabby and bleak without the tree. I carried the jelly jars to the sink, unwilling to look at the empty space.

192

"It's still not too late to get the tree back," Jim said as he put his arms around me.

"No. It belongs here in Oz. I want Harry to have it."

"Oz?"

"I feel like Dorothy going back to Kansas. Do you remember the movie?"

He nodded.

"Kansas was black and white, it was real. Dorothy lived a hard life there. Oh, Jim . . ." I started to cry.

"Leo, darling. What is it? What's wrong?"

"What if Iowa is black and white? What if we can't make it there?"

"Of course we can. You remember how Dorothy gets back, don't you?"

"I remember that she wanted to go home very badly."

"Iowa is going to be *our* home, Leo."

"I know, that's what scares me."

"But why? It's what we've worked so hard for."

"I know. But don't you realize we don't know what it is to be ordinary? What we've had here in New York is our honeymoon. It's over, and we just got married this afternoon. We've never even had an argument. I'm afraid of what will happen once we settle down into an ordinary routine."

"So who's ordinary, Leo?"

He kissed me softly. I felt something turn over and settle inside me. Whatever was going to happen to me was in God's hands. Not mine.

All things considered, He hadn't done badly by me at all.